BROTHERS

NO MORE

BROTHERS

NO MORE

by Lee Rebsom

Published by Kremer Publishing
2023
P.O. Box 1385
Osprey, FL 34229-1385
www.KevinKremerBooks.com

Special thanks to:

The North Dakota Humanities Council for sponsoring writing classes. Those classes were invaluable in writing this book.

A gifted instructor who diligently instructed, encouraged, and inspired me.

A special friend who read my first rough draft. His interest and enthusiasm propelled me to continue.

Everyone who helped by reviewing and editing my writing. I know it wasn't an easy task, but you all came through.

A special thank you to my wife and daughters who helped with everything from connecting me with a publisher, editing, and cover design. Your help and support throughout the process were much appreciated.

*This book is dedicated to Vietnam Veterans—
the ones who endured and the ones who never
got the chance to endure.*

CONTENTS

Brothers

Winter hung over the countryside like a white blanket covering everything with a thick layer of snow piled to such enormous depths that in places it obliterated the landscape. Daily prevailing winds kept the snow in motion making life on the Northern Great Plains a challenge especially in the dead of winter. What would appear as a despondent and forlorn place was actually full of life, with struggles for daily survival between predator and prey unfolding on a regular basis.

The wind blew constantly. Temperatures 30 degrees below zero in the winter were common, and combined with the wind, created hazardous conditions for man and beast. In the summer temperatures would soar into the 90s and scorch the landscape.

Three young boys growing up in the center of such a vast and varied environment could only become predators. It was man against nature at the very pinnacle of extremes.

Their father and mother, Joe and Helen O'Janon, had both immigrated to America as young children with their families, enticed by the Homestead Act and the opportunities it presented for a better life.

What had been vast hunting grounds for the American Indians was taken over by European immigrants. They tried to tame and civilize the land, but Mother Nature is a strong force to be reckoned with. Wildlife that had seemingly disappeared adapted and resurfaced. It was these resilient survivors that the three young brothers were pitted against. Winter primed the pelts of all wildlife, both predator and prey. A virtual cash crop provided by Mother Nature was available to those resourceful enough to outsmart and outmaneuver wildlife in their own environment.

The brothers had no way of knowing what the skills they were learning would prepare them for, but their father knew. His military uniform hung over the stairway leading downstairs to their bedroom, a daily reminder of the skills that would be necessary if his boys were called to serve their country. Their world seemed very normal to them, but to someone from the outside, it would have appeared very harsh and uncivilized, with a touch of wild thrown in for good measure.

FAITHFUL

WE WERE FAITHFUL

OUR COUNTRY WAS NOT

Chapter 1
First Gun

The first weapon the brothers received was a Daisy lever-action BB gun. Jake was five, Jay was six, and John was seven years old. To them, it was a momentous event.

The BB gun was never out of their sight. One or the other always had it in hand whenever they left the house. At first, they even slept with it, until their mother, Helen, discovered what they were doing. They would borrow their dad's gun oil and constantly clean the BB gun to keep it spotless. If one of them dropped or mishandled the gun, he would instantly face the ire of the other two.

The stock on the BB gun was too long for any of them, especially Jake. They couldn't shoulder it properly, but through trial and error they adapted and became quite proficient at shooting the BB gun.

One afternoon Uncle Hugo, their favorite neighbor, stopped over to borrow some tools from their dad. The brothers took this opportunity to proudly show him their new BB gun. They immediately set up an empty tin can to show off their shooting skills. Soon a challenge ensued, and Uncle Hugo was handed the BB gun to see if his shooting skills could match theirs. The brothers had all shot from the prone position, lying flat on the ground. Uncle Hugo shot standing, and he easily outshot all three of them. Afterward he carefully examined the BB gun and said, "Bring it over some day, and I will fix it so it will fit you boys better."

With their parents' permission, the next morning they saddled their ponies and rode over to Uncle Hugo's farm. He was still eating breakfast when he was startled by three very eager young boys. Shaking his head, he said, "My, you boys are serious! I'm sure glad I made *these* last night. I just haven't painted them yet."

Uncle Hugo showed them six wooden silhouette targets which he had made for them. There were two life-sized bird targets that were attached to small horizontal wooden stands which kept them upright, plus two gophers and two crows, all on wooden stands.

The boys were in awe and immediately asked if they could go outside and shoot them. Uncle Hugo said, "Before we do that, we'll go to the shop, and I will make some adjustments to your gun while you boys paint the targets. I'm going to finish my breakfast now. Are you boys hungry? I can make you some eggs if you want."

Wanting to shoot at the targets as soon as possible, all Uncle Hugo heard was a resounding, "No, thank you."

After Uncle Hugo had finished his breakfast, the boys helped him clean up the table and wash the dishes. They anxiously followed him out to his shop, carefully carrying the new targets. When they got to the shop, Uncle Hugo dug around on some shelving and pulled out two cans of paint, one white and one black. Then Uncle Hugo had the boys mix the paint. After that, he pulled out a small empty bucket and poured some white paint and black paint into it and had the boys mix the two colors together to make a gray color. After they were done mixing the gray paint, Uncle Hugo gave them some paint brushes and told the boys, "Paint the birds white, the crows black, and the gophers gray while I fix your gun."

They got to work painting but kept an eye on Uncle Hugo. First, he wrapped their gun in an old towel. Then he placed it into his workbench vice, tightened up the vice, pulled down a yardstick from the pegboard above his workbench, and he did some measuring.

When he pulled down a wood saw, the boys' looks must have given them away because Uncle Hugo said, "Boys, trust me. I know what I'm doing." Then he began sawing off the back part of the BB gun's stock while he hummed an old Swedish ballad.

John could see that Jay was becoming extremely concerned about their gun. He was too, but he knew that Uncle Hugo was an expert with guns, and a lot of neighbors brought theirs over to him for repairs. John motioned to Jay to calm down.

After he had sawed off the back end of the stock, Uncle Hugo did some more measuring, then pulled some sandpaper from a drawer and gently sanded the stock where it had been sawed off. He unscrewed the butt plate from the sawed-off end and screwed it onto the new end of the now shortened stock. Then he dug out a file and filed the butt plate down to match the new edge of the shortened stock.

After he was done with the stock, he pulled out a small, thin file and began filing on the rear sight which almost made Jay go ballistic, but with a nod from John he kept quiet. Uncle Hugo removed the BB gun from the vice and brought it up to his shoulder and viewed down the sights. A slight smile of satisfaction appeared on his face as he placed the gun back down onto his workbench with the old towel under it and pulled a scribe out of a drawer and began inscribing something onto the stock while Jay watched nervously. After Uncle Hugo was done, he brought down a can of stain which he applied to the stock where he had inscribed something into the wood.

Uncle Hugo turned and asked, "Well boys, are the targets dry yet?"

John answered, "They would be if Jake would just stop repainting them."

John and Jay both gave Jake a disgusted look which he ignored. The targets were painted perfectly because of him, and he was proud of them.

Uncle Hugo said, "Well, let's clean up the paint brushes and put things away, then we'll go check some cows while the targets dry. When we get back, we will see how you boys do with your new gun."

They were dying to get their hands on the gun, mostly to make sure that Uncle Hugo hadn't ruined it. He wouldn't let them see or handle the BB gun until the targets were dry.

They reluctantly climbed into Uncle Hugo's old 1945 green Ford pickup which he drove out to a pasture where he had moved his herd of cows a few days earlier. The trip seemed to take forever as Uncle Hugo drove slowly through the pasture stopping frequently to get out and view a cow or calf more closely from all angles.

"I thought I saw her limping" or "her calf looked like it might be getting sick" were his typical comments every time he returned to the pickup from a short jaunt. Finally, he said, "Well, everything looks fine here. Let's go back and see how your gun fits and shoots."

When they arrived back at his yard, Uncle Hugo had the brothers bring out the targets and place the two bird silhouettes on fence posts and the gopher silhouettes on the ground a short distance from the fence. Then he had the boys bring two empty one-gallon pails out and place them on the ground closer to where they would be shooting from and set one crow on top of each pail.

Uncle Hugo instructed them to wait at the firing line as he went into the shop and exited, proudly carrying their BB gun which he presented to them. "What do you boys think?" he asked.

They took turns handling, sighting, and viewing their refurbished gun. They were all amazed at how well it fit each one of them and how easy it was to sight through the filed-out rear sight.

They all questioned the neatly inscribed words on the stock. All three of them wanted to know what *Rast ich so Rost ich* meant. Uncle Hugo explained how an old German gunsmith used to inscribe those words into the steel action of every rifle he made. It meant *When I rest, I rust*.

"Now, you boys must remember these words of wisdom from a gifted and wise man. He isn't just referring to the gun. He also means *you*. If you want to be good at shooting, you must shoot."

He showed them how they were overlubricating the gun and explained how keeping the gun clean and lubricated was important. Too much gun oil was just as bad as not enough and could even cause function issues in extremely cold conditions which could cause the gun oil to become stiff and gummy.

He had them take turns shooting at the targets from prone, sitting, and standing positions. It was great fun for the boys watching a bird, gopher, or crow tumble over after it was hit.

They all thanked Uncle Hugo as they left the yard with the targets in a gunny sack secured to John's saddle horn. They couldn't wait to get home and show their parents the gun and targets. Uncle Hugo bellowed out *"Rast ich so Rost ich!"* as he waved to the boys.

Their dad encouraged them shoot sparrows who had taken up residence within the numerous ranch buildings. He did not mind the sparrows, but their population had increased to the point that he became worried about them becoming sick from overpopulation and then spreading a disease to the livestock. As an extra incentive, the brothers received a penny for each sparrow shot and killed.

The hunting was easy until the sparrows wised up and forced the brothers to learn how to carefully stalk within BB gun range. They also built elaborate snipers' nests to hide in while waiting patiently for sparrows to come within range. Their dad always complimented and encouraged them, but sometimes the boys had to press him pretty hard to get the pennies.

The three brothers spent their free time practicing shooting at the silhouette targets from Uncle Hugo, or they would head down to the river bottoms or a pasture to hunt small animals like mice, gophers, frogs, or birds. They discovered that Jake's stupid whistle sound he made while trying to learn to whistle would bring gophers out of their burrows. John and Jay even practiced trying to imitate Jake's sound. Their mother would not allow them to do it in the house after she had heard it one too many times.

Their dad had sat them down and given them a verbal list of what they could shoot with the BB gun. He told them that shooting anything larger would only cause minor wounds, and he would not allow them to injure or harass larger wildlife. He also instructed them how to properly operate and load the BB gun, and he emphasized that it was a weapon. They were to never point it at each other or anyone else. The brothers strictly adhered to their dad's instructions because they did not want to lose the BB gun.

Their mother hired a local high school girl from town during the summer to do household chores and watch over her boys while she assisted their dad during the haying season. Three young boys could test the patience of anyone, and most of the teenage high school girls lasted only one summer, until Eddie came along.

Eddie was able to do all the household chores and maintain control of the boys at the same time. She seemed to have eyes in the back of her head. She usually knew where they were and what they were up to no matter how sneaky they were. They just couldn't get away with much when Eddie was around. Eddie was fair, but the brothers thought that she took her responsibilities way too seriously. She made sure that their chores were completed before they could play and would join them in games if she had her own chores done. She also broke up occasional boyhood disputes, but only if it appeared that things were getting out of hand. Otherwise, the boys were allowed to settle the matter on their own terms.

One day Jay came up with a plan which he presented to John and Jake. Jay wanted to shoot Eddie in the butt with the BB gun from what they deemed a safe distance so it would only sting her, and then they'd see if she would pull down her pants to check the damage. Why John and Jake let Jay talk them into the plan when they knew better was a topic they discussed well into their teenage years. After some discussion they went into stalk mode. Eddie was hanging clothes on the clothesline in the backyard where the nearby shelter belt offered them perfect cover for the stalk.

After Eddie felt the BB hit her, she didn't pull down her pants as they had planned, but she *did* turn them in. After they were disciplined, they wished they had never thought up or completed the stunt because they were the ones with sore butts, and the BB gun disappeared for a while. That was the last time they ever pointed a gun at another person until the Army took them to the dark shadows of war.

Eddie didn't have brothers, and it took her a while to understand certain boyhood behaviors, but eventually she forgave the brothers. They began to view her as a big sister who cared about them and someone they could trust. Eddie came back every summer for three more years until she left for college. By then the brothers were out in the hay fields, and hired girls were a distant memory.

DON'T GET TOO CLOSE

WILLING TO DIE FOR YOU

JUST DON'T HAVE THE WILL TO GRIEVE FOR YOU

CHAPTER 2
Country School

Heading out to school on a crisp fall morning, John, Jay, and Jake trudged along the two-track dirt trail leading to the top of Zingers Hill. They instinctively stopped just before reaching the crest to scan the undulating prairie ahead of them, searching for wildlife.

The ranch buildings were visible two miles behind them. One mile ahead stood the white-washed one room schoolhouse that was their destination. It sat stoically on the prairie with a small red barn and two white outhouses in the background. After a quick scan, John and Jake resumed the daily hike to school. As usual, Jay stayed put, scanning then running to catch up with them. About a quarter of a mile from the school, they safely stashed their BB gun which was not allowed on the school's property.

Six other families from the surrounding area also sent children to the school for an education for grades one through eight. All eight grades were taught by one teacher. The brothers could see fellow classmates arriving from different directions. Some of them were getting rides, others were walking. Then there was Butch, coming from the south on his pony.

Butch hated walking. He had outgrown the pony long ago but continued to use him as transportation to get to school and for trips to surrounding neighbors. The pony created a little dust trail as he slowly trudged along the country trail leading to the school. Butch looked ridiculous riding the pony, but he could care less as he wasn't walking and that's all that mattered.

The brothers arrived at school early and so did everyone else. As if on cue, *Oscar Ya-Ya*, an older student, came out of the schoolhouse. He got the nickname because he began every conversation with the phrase *Ya-Ya*, accompanied by a slight head bob. He was carrying two buckets full of ashes from the coal stove in the basement.

The stove provided radiant heat to the school through two oversized floor registers located on the north side of the uninsulated building. Girls and younger children were assigned to the desks located on the north side of the classroom, while the boys' desks were on the south side of the room, which featured a solid row of windows that ran almost the entire length of the buildings south side.

Oscar's head bobbed as he said, "Ya-Ya, it's going to be a cold one today, so I cleaned out the furnace, loaded it with new coal, and lit it." Oscar disliked cold and kept a very watchful eye on the furnace.

Slim's mom pulled up to the school's front door in a dusty 1953 Chevy. Slim would get a ride to and from school every day that week because it was his family's turn to haul water for the school and provide a noon meal for all the students and the teacher for the entire week.

John helped Slim carry in a cream can full of water and fill the school's Red Wing water cooler located in the entryway. Jay helped Slim's mom carry in the noon meal and received an early brownie for his efforts which he would not share. Jay was the lady charmer of the brothers, even at an early age. Later in the morning the noon meal would be heated up on two electric hot plates.

When the teacher rang the bell, everyone entered the school and stood solemnly beside their desks. They faced the flag at the front of the school room, placed their right hand over their hearts, and recited the Pledge of Allegiance in unison.

Miss Redmond, the teacher, was a petite woman who was very passionate about teaching. When it came to discipline, if you had it coming, you got it. Then, for good measure, you got it some more. She ran a very efficient and well-organized school and was John's teacher for seven of his eight years at the country school.

Separate classes for each grade were held on benches in a back corner of the room while the rest of the classes worked on their assignments in small groups around the room. There was never any homework. All assignments were completed at school.

There were two major social events held at the school every year. The first was an annual Christmas program featuring all the students. It was held at the school for parents the last evening before Christmas break began. A stage area was built at the front of the schoolroom using sheets strung over suspended wires. Costumes were sewn by mothers, and any necessary props were built by the older students. The students practiced assigned plays and songs during recess periods. Musical instruments were practiced at home to the delight of parents and siblings.

Howard, the school comedian, was usually given the leading part in the main school play. To everyone's surprise, Howard always took this very seriously. Patty, who had a beautiful voice, always sang a solo Christmas song. The brothers never enjoyed participating in plays or singing in the choir, but they performed to the best of their abilities.

One year their mom decided that Jay should learn how to play a violin uke which she had picked up at an auction sale that fall, and then play a song for the upcoming Christmas program. Shortly after Jay began practicing playing the violin uke, it mysteriously suffered damage that rendered it unusable. None of the brothers were responsible for the damage, but they were the ones held account-able by their mother. They deemed the discipline well worth the loss and never asked their dad about it.

The second major school event was Play Day which was held every spring. Play Day was track and field based, consisting of various competitive outdoor events. There were competitions geared toward students of various ages, and there was usually a surprise event dreamed up by the teachers.

All the rural schools located in the school district participated. Play Day was held in a larger town school nearby because of the number of students participating. The students were divided into four age groups to keep the competitions fair. Ribbons were given out to the winners of each competition, but the main prize was bragging rights.

To get ready for Play Day, the boys at the school built a broad jump pit, high jump stand, and measured off distances for various running competitions. Recesses before a Play Day event were always spent practicing.

Competition between the boys from different schools would become fierce at times, resulting in boyhood scraps often erupting during or after events. Foot races usually became push and shove races, especially when Jay was participating.

Girls competed against each other in the same events as the boys. Some of them would have beaten the boys in their age groups if they had been allowed to compete with them. The girls' events were always completed in a more civil and organized manner than the boys' events.

Teachers were kept extremely busy trying to control various groups of young boys. A deputy sheriff from the county sheriff's department located down the street from the town's school was usually present to assist the teachers. The assigned deputy was usually not in a good mood, and it only took one visit to the deputy for an unruly boy to become a model Play Day participant.

The grand finale were tug-of-war competitions between schools, with the losing team being dragged into a sand pit separating the teams. The school the brothers attended had never lost a tug-of-war competition because of their secret weapon, Tubby. Tubby was as big around as he was tall, and when he grabbed the rope in the anchor position, he was immovable. He enjoyed dragging an opposing team into the sand pit, especially if it had rained the night before. Tubby would laugh and talk about the tug-of-war match for weeks afterwards.

Recesses at the school were full of outdoor activities. Many included all the children from grades one through eight. The student body was like one big neighborhood family. Most of the students had younger or older siblings at home and playing together was normal for them.

In the winter elaborate snow forts were built

and wars fought between opposing teams utilizing snowballs. Students would also bring their sleds to school. Many recess periods were spent riding down a nearby hill in the snow. The boys usually turned sled riding into competitions like racing or sled derbies which pitted two boys on a sled against other teams trying to knock opposing team members off their sleds while sledding down the hill. Slim, who was slender and very breakable, seemed to suffer an injury a week sled riding, but he always came back for more.

Another winter activity was Fox and the Goose. To play the game, a large circle resembling a wagon wheel was stomped out in the snow along with spokes coming out from a safe area in the center. There were also safe areas located at the junctions of the spokes and the outer wheel circle. Two people would be designated as foxes and the rest were geese. Players could only stay within a safe area for five seconds and then they had to sprint to another. Players were not allowed to step out of the circle or spoke tracks, and this was sometimes difficult to do while running from one safe area to another at full speed on slippery snow wearing cumbersome overshoes.

The two foxes would chase and tag the geese. Once tagged, the goose would step out of the circle, and the game would continue until all the geese had been tagged. The fox with the most geese would become the winner. A lot of the time the tagging would turn into tackling.

Ice hockey, another favorite that used sticks and cans, was played on a nearby livestock dam. Any snow on the ice was first removed from the dam with scoop shovels that the boys would bring from home. No one had skates. Overshoes were removed and movement was accomplished by trying to run and then slide. Kissing the Ice, which is what the boys called falling down on the ice, happened frequently. The games would become fierce events with a lot of pushing and shoving taking place. Everyone would go home with bumps and bruises from falls and continually getting hit by the sticks. John once watched a hockey game on TV and when the announcer called it a rough game he thought, "Well, he's never played stick hockey on a frozen stock pond."

Warm weather activities included softball games which could get heated at times because the students umpired themselves. The team that made the most noise usually won.

Annie-Annie Over utilizing the little red barn roof was another fun game often played. The school children divided themselves into two groups and would place themselves on either side of the barn. A softball was then thrown over the roof from one team to the other as they shouted out *Annie-Annie Over*! The receiving team would catch the ball and give it to their fastest player or someone else that the other team would never expect to be the tagger. This was the only person who could tag an opponent. Then the whole team would run around the barn, and their tagger would try to tag players on the other team before they could run around to the other side of the barn.

Sometimes a team would split their players into two groups. One group ran around one side of the barn. The other group, with a tagger holding back for a few seconds, ran around to the other side of the barn. They might also all run around the barn with one hand behind their backs so the other team couldn't identify the tagger until it was too late.

Once you were tagged, you were on that team. The play continued until all of the players wound up on the same team.

When the weather permitted, most of the boys went swimming in a nearby livestock dam during their lunch hour which usually resulted in mud fights. No one really knew how to swim, but they were able to stay afloat by dog paddling. Some kids would hang onto an old dead tree that had been dragged down to the dam and placed into the water where it floated around at will.

There were also swings, a teeter totter, and a merry-go-round for the younger children at the school. If not playing a game, the boys always found something to occupy themselves. No weapons of any kind were allowed on the school grounds, so the boys used rocks and sticks to terrorize the local gopher, bird, frog, and snake populations. Any animals killed were placed in the girls' outhouse. This was never well received by the girls, but it was a tradition that the boys continued with pride.

There was also an annual YCL (Young Citizens League) speaking competition that was held every year at a larger town school. Each country and town school in the county was required to send two students to participate.

John was chosen to be one of the participants every year starting in the fifth grade until he graduated because of his *resounding* voice, as Miss Redmond described it. John hated having to write a speech and then to get up in front of dozens of strange kids and present it. John would have to pick a patriotic subject, and Miss Redmond would review the speech and have John practice speaking it in front of his classmates.

John usually came home with a first place mostly because of the American Indian kids who were also required to attend the annual competition. John would hang out with them on breaks, and for some reason, rather than voting for one of their own, they would all vote for him.

One year an American Indian that was John's age named Tyrone Spotted Horse gave a great speech. During a break, John approached Tyrone, congratulated him on his speech, and told Tyrone he thought he could win the competition.

Tyrone responded, "No, we're all voting for you."

John asked, "Why vote for me when my

speech isn't as good as yours?"

Tyrone answered, "Because we are outnumbered. No white kids will vote for an Indian, and you're the nicest white kid here."

"Well, that just isn't right," John replied. "I'm voting for the best speech no matter what."

Miss Redmond thought John was the best speaker in the county and kept sending him to the competition no matter how hard he protested.

The daily walk to and from school was usually broken up by wildlife, various livestock, and any other distractions that could hold the attention of three young boys. One fall morning they decided to sneak some traps out of the trapping shed and set them along the route to school.

A few afternoons later, on the way home they discovered a skunk was caught in one of the traps. This was their first success at trapping, and in their excitement, they took turns trying to kill it with their BB gun. This only enraged the skunk, resulting in each one of them getting sprayed by it. When they got home, they reeked so bad from the skunk's spray that Helen made them take off all their clothes which she washed immediately. Then she had them take baths outside in an old, galvanized tub before entering the house.

That evening their dad went out and shot the skunk and then he dispatched some discipline to the brothers. Later that fall, he showed them how to trap and gave them an old single shot Remington Model 4 rolling block 22 rimfire rifle to shoot any future animals caught in traps. The 22 rimfire rifle resulted in the demise of the BB gun. A whole new world had just been opened for the brothers. Now anything except larger animals like deer or antelope was fair game.

From then on, the brothers maintained a trap line around the ranch every winter to trap various fur-bearing animals. Two of the brothers would stay and do assigned chores before leaving for school while the other one checked the trap line. Their dad supported their efforts, but he insisted that the chores came first, and if they were not completed, the trapping would cease. Anything caught during the night was dispatched with the 22 rimfire rifle, brought back to the ranch, and placed in the trapping shed.

After school and evening chores were done, the pelts would be removed by skinning with knives, then the inside of each pelt would be scraped clean with scrapers designed for that purpose. Next, they were stretched inside out to dry on special stretchers built by their dad. After the pelts had dried, they were taken off the stretchers, turned again with the fur side out, and combed and cleaned if necessary to make them ready for sale.

Just about every town had a business that bought farm animal hides and wild animal fur pelts. There were also independent buyers who supplemented their income buying and selling hides and furs. The brothers were always searching for the buyers who paid more than others. They were usually paid 50 cents for a weasel pelt, $10 for mink, and up to $15 for a large blanket beaver. Fox pelts could drop to as low as $2 and coyotes usually sold between $10 and $20. For one reason or another, fur markets fluctuated season to season, and some years certain animal pelts sold for amazing prices, and other years you had to almost give them away.

The brothers hunted and trapped as much as possible, but the ranch always came first. Their dad saw to that.

FIRST BLOOD

ALWAYS WATCH A NEW GUY

BECAUSE FIRST BLOOD TELLS A LOT

CHAPTER 3
Ranch Life

At the age of 10 each brother was given a small herd of four cows. The income derived from selling the cows' calves in the fall was theirs to spend as they saw fit. From then on, medical care plus room and board were all that they received from their parents. Everything needed for school and personal use was purchased with income made from selling the calves.

Their mother helped them budget because payday only came once a year in the fall when their calves were sold at a local sales barn. She was also the banker and kept the money tucked away until they needed it. Extra income was earned from hunting, trapping, and working for neighbors as time allowed.

Every summer was spent working on the ranch. That was how the brothers paid their dad for their cows' upkeep. Only once did the entire family leave the ranch. They went to Canada to visit their dad's only sister, who was having health issues.

Occasionally, their mother would take one of the boys to Minnesota or Montana by train for a short visit to one of her sisters. The other two would stay home to help their dad with the ranch. The only complaint was Dad's cooking as he only knew how to prepare one meal, macaroni and cheese.

Life began at 5:00 a.m. every morning. Joe would come downstairs, turn the lights on, and shout out, "Time to get rolling! What do you boys think this is, a laying around joint?"

Morning always began with the milk cows. There were usually four to six of them, and they were all milked by hand. They were gathered up and put in the milking barn then given some grain to help keep them calm. Some mornings one cow or the other would get cranky because they had run out of grain or whatever makes a cow cranky, and they would kick the milking pail over, usually when it was almost full. They seemed to constantly swish their tails, even without flies bothering them, and the boys hated getting whacked in the head.

After being milked, the cows were turned out into a feed yard in the winter and a pasture during the summer. Next, they fed the orphaned pail calves. Then they fed their mom's chickens and gathered up any eggs that had been laid overnight. Taking care of Dad's pigs was their least favorite chore. There were usually a few horses penned up somewhere that required feeding, and this was their favorite morning chore. Horses were clean, friendly, and they definitely smelled better than the pigs, chickens, or cows.

After morning chores came breakfast, then it was on to whatever activity their dad had planned for the day. If it was a school day, they headed out for school.

During the summer, haying seemed to take up most of their time. It seemed to go on forever, moving from one field to another, and just when the end was in sight, the second cutting was ready to go.

Haying began with mowing. Dad would get one of the John Deere B tractors. To start it required opening two petcock valves located on each side of the engine and then spinning a big flywheel that was mounted on one side of the tractor by hand until the tractor started. The boys couldn't accomplish this until they got older.

The tractor had a steel seat that was burning hot in the summer heat and freezing cold in the winter. There was a hand clutch mounted on the right side of the operator's platform, plus a steering wheel, gear shift lever, throttle, power take-off control lever, and two brake pedals.

A nine-foot sickle mower was hooked up to the tractor's drawbar. The power take-off unit at the back of the tractor was connected to the mower. You began haying by going around and around a field starting on the outside and mowing your way to the center until all the hay was lying on the ground ready to air dry.

Determining the hay's moisture content by feel was a learned function that the brothers were taught by their dad. A handful of hay was picked up and twisted while feeling for moisture. If the hay was determined to be dry enough, it was then raked into windrows using a second John Deere B tractor to pull an eleven-foot power take-off side delivery rake in much the same manner as mowing. This was done by starting on the outside and then going around and around raking until the center was reached and the hay was laid out in windrows for baling.

Baling was accomplished using a John Deere A tractor which was more powerful than the B John Deere tractors. The A had an engine mounted starter that was powered by a six-volt battery and a larger operating platform than the B's. It also had a foot clutch and cushioned seat which was considered a luxury. A John Deere square baler was hooked up to the John Deere A's drawbar, and the power take-off connected to the baler. Then the around and around procedure began all over again until all the hay was lying in the field in 40-pound bales ready for transport to one of the numerous hay yards located on the ranch.

Square hay balers had a complicated string

tying mechanism that required constant tinker-
ing. Operating a square hay baler could become
frustrating, but if you persisted, producing properly tied and compacted bales would eventually be
accomplished. The brothers' dad was a master at
timing and maintaining a square baler and neighbors would constantly request his assistance.

John became fairly adept at operating the
baler, but at times he would become frustrated
trying to keep the timing and string tying mechanism operating properly. Jake easily mastered
baling and was very skilled at keeping everything
operating perfectly. He eventually became a better operator than their dad. Jay just couldn't master operating a baler, so he did a lot of the mowing
and raking. Once they got started, there were
sometimes three tractors operating in different
fields at once, one pulling the mower, one pulling
the rake, and one pulling the baler.

Hauling was accomplished by hand using old,
three-tine, bundle forks that their dad had kept
around from the old days when they would thresh
grain. The brothers would hacksaw off the tines
about halfway up, then file them to sharp points.
Bales were removed from the hay fields as soon as
possible to avoid weather damage to the hay from
rain which would cause a decline in the quality of
the hay.

The bales were pitched by hand using the
bundle forks onto a flatbed trailer pulled by one of
the John Deere B tractors. One of the brothers

would pitch bales to another brother who rode the trailer and stacked the bales for transport. The third one drove the tractor. There was no stopping. Pitching the bales onto the trailer and stacking them on it was accomplished with the tractor pulling the trailer down the numerous rows of bales in a lower gear. They rotated positions every load. After the trailer was loaded, it was pulled to a hay yard and unloaded. Then it was restacked again into stacks that were now ready for winter feeding.

The bottoms where the hay fields were located kept the procedure of going around and around a field from becoming boring. A tree-lined river sliced through the center of the bottoms, snaking back and forth, making the shape of each field unique. Constant attention was required because nothing was linear within the fields. Numerous wildlife also lived within the bottoms, and it was always exciting to see newborn deer fawns and pheasant chicks accompanying their mothers.

Haying was labor intensive and time consuming, but it was necessary to ensure the ranch livestock's survival through the long and brutal winters that were typical in the Northern Great Plains region where the ranch was located. Their dad would remind the boys at the beginning of every haying season, "Always be ready for a hard winter because if it comes and you're not ready, it's too late." The ranch was always ready!

One of the best moments on the ranch every

year for the brothers was when they finished stacking the last load of bales onto a stack for the season. They would cross their arms and stand elbow to elbow gazing at the last stack for a moment with the same thought, *The ranch is ready.*

On occasion, if time permitted, the brothers would haul bales for the surrounding neighbors. They were paid three cents per bale for this. It didn't seem like much, but if they could move 1,000 bales in a day, they each made $10 for a day's labor which was a lot of money for them.

When time allowed, the brothers also summer fallowed for the neighbors. Summer fallowing was a system of farming used when a field was only planted with a small grain crop every other year. The year that it wasn't seeded, it was tilled multiple times during the summer with a cultivator pulled behind a tractor to control weed growth within the field. It required going around and around like haying, only you were tilling up the soil. It was a dirty, dusty, hot, and boring job. Summer fallowing did not pay much, but the brothers did it for their neighbors when they could.

If they wanted to do work for their neighbors, the brothers knew they had to ask their dad for permission. The ranch always came first. Jay didn't manage his money as well as his brothers, and he seemed to always be seeking permission to work for neighbors. His dad would then remind him how much it cost to feed and maintain his cows on the ranch for a year.

Fencing also kept the brothers busy. Winter's snow raised havoc with the numerous fences located on the ranch. They required repair or replacement every spring before the livestock could be placed in the pastures. The cows and wildlife did their share of damage to the fences too, and they needed to be repaired immediately to keep the cows where they belonged.

Fencing was labor intensive. Post holes for wooden fence posts were dug by hand using a hand-operated post hole digger. Steel posts were pounded into the ground by hand using a steel post driver. Eighty-pound rolls of fencing wire were unrolled by placing a steel rod through the center of the roll. Two of the brothers, one on each end of the rod, would then lift and carry the roll of wire up and down numerous pasture hills along fence lines, unrolling the wire.

One year their dad purchased an adjoining section of pastureland that was not fenced. To use the land for grazing, they first had to fence the perimeter. One morning while fencing, John reached into some grass to retrieve a steel fence post and stuck his bare hand into a cactus patch. He was in extreme pain as their dad pulled the cactus spines from his hand with a set of pliers. He finally began crying out as each spine was being pulled out.

Their dad kept saying, "You're tougher than that! Don't let a little thing like a cactus bother you."

When all the spines were removed, the fencing was resumed until noon when they stopped for sandwiches that their mom had packed for them. Their dad wasn't paying attention and plopped down right in the middle of a cactus patch. He was clearly in pain, and he immediately pulled down his pants and had John and Jay begin pulling out the cactus spines. Just like John, he began crying out as each spine was pulled. John and Jay began smirking as they pulled spines from their dad's stark white butt while silently mouthing, "Don't let a little thing like a cactus bother you."

If not haying or fencing, their dad always had something in mind for the boys, and it seemed as if the work never ended. He told them numerous times, "There's no reason to be bored if there's work to be done," and the boys were never bored. They learned how to perform general maintenance and repairs on the equipment used for haying and grain harvesting. Their dad also had a collection of old horse-drawn equipment, some of which he still used. It required maintenance and periodic repairs which somehow became the sole responsibility of the brothers.

The brothers had never met their grandparents on their dad's side as they both had passed away before any of the boys were born. There were pictures and stories of their grandparents, but the horse-drawn equipment was a physical part of their grandfather's legacy, and they inadvertently came to know a part of him through operating and maintaining the machinery.

Grandma had left her recipes and their mother prepared meals from them. As she was serving the food, she always reminded them, "This was your grandma's cooking." They also learned about their grandma's garden which featured an ornate metal entrance gate custom built by a local blacksmith. One corner was devoted to prairie flowers and forbs and another corner contained the best rhubarb in the county. Helen told them their grandmother had brought the rhubarb plants over from the old country.

The hardest maintenance project for the brothers was greasing the wagon wheels on the hay rack. Grandpa used the hay rack to haul bundles of wheat from fields to a stationary threshing machine to harvest the grain. It was now used to haul feed to the cattle. This job required an old giant screw jack that took a couple of them to carry. First, they loosened the huge nut holding the wooden wheel in place with a special wrench which they were instructed to never misplace. Then they pushed, pulled, and shoved the screw jack under the hay rack and lifted the frame up enough to remove the wooden wheel. This required all three of them working together to remove the wheel while trying not to drop it onto themselves. Then they greased the wheel shaft and the inside of the wheel with a special wagon wheel grease that their dad purchased at an old blacksmith shop located quite a distance from the ranch. After that, they put the wheel back on, and then they were on to the next wheel.

A team of horses was hitched to the hay rack and used to feed cattle in the winter before the snow got too deep. When the snow became too deep for the hayrack, the team was hitched to a bobsled which was made for use in snow to haul hay bales to the cattle. The bobsled ran on four wooden runners. The front two pivoted to aid in steering. The runners had steel plates riveted to their bottoms. The bobsled had a front and sides that were about three feet high and made from wood with a removable end gate. The bobsled was also used on extreme winter days to transport the brothers to and from school.

An old five-foot horse-drawn sickle mower was used every summer to mow around the ranch buildings. The cutting sickle on the mower was ground driven by two steel wheels, one on each side of the mower, that supported the mower. A shaft from the center of each wheel was connected to a gear box located on the inside of the cutting sickle which propelled the sickle bar back and forth, cutting whatever was in its path. The steel wheels had one-inch steel plates riveted in rows around the entire wheel to ensure that there were no interruptions in the mowing system from wheel slippage. Beside the seat was one lever. It was used to raise the cutter bar if needed. The horse-drawn mower would not cut unless it was moving.

Their dad also had a wooden buggy with tall, thin, wooden wheels with steel riveted on the outside of them. It had a spring-loaded seat with a shallow wooden box behind it. There were small metal pedal steps located at the front and back to get up into it.

The buggy was used every spring to cross over the bottoms during spring flooding. A car would be parked across the bottoms early every spring on high ground for their mom and dad to get to town if necessary. The buggy was also used to get the boys to and from school during the spring flooding. A team would be hitched to the buggy, the boys would crawl up into the box, and their dad would carefully guide the team across the flooded bottoms. Their dad sat on the seat firmly holding the two long bridle reins that were attached to the horses' bridles and ran back to the buggy through leather loops that were sewn into the harness. He usually took the boys all the way to school unless he had to get home to check up on a cow and be there to help pull her calf if she was having problems. Then the boys walked the rest of the way to school.

The boys' least favorite piece of horse-drawn equipment was the manure spreader because it always involved pitching manure by hand from barns and corral fence lines onto it using manure forks. There were forks for everything—pitching loose hay forks, bailed hay forks, manure forks, coal forks, bundle forks, and even potato forks for digging up potatoes.

The manure spreader was built of wood with a steel frame on the underside. The conveyor on the bottom of the spreader was made of wooden slats riveted to steel conveyor chains. It moved the manure to the rear where a steel paddlewheel spread it onto the ground. The conveyor and paddlewheel were ground driven by the two large steel wheels located at the rear of the spreader like the mower's system. Two steel wheels were up front which pivoted to follow the team. A steel seat for the team driver was located up front with a control lever to stop or start the spreader. This had to be done while the spreader was stationary so you wouldn't break an arm or leg near the lever because it would violently snap from one position to another if not locked when the spreader was in motion.

Molly and Dolly, matching jet-black Percheron work horses, would be brought into the barn and placed, one at a time, between two raised platforms built by the brothers that resembled the bottom seat on a set of bleachers. The platforms enabled them to get the harnesses up and over the huge work horses. They also used the platforms to get the heavy, cumbersome neck yokes up and over their necks into position above the horses' front shoulders.

Molly and Dolly usually exhibited fair temperament unless one of them was in their monthly breeding cycle which seemed to affect both horses. Molly always pulled harder than Dolly who was a bit of a slacker requiring a slap on the rump now and then to make her pull her fair share. When they were hitched to the manure spreader, the two horses seemed to enjoy hauling and spreading manure about as much as the brothers did.

There was one annual event connected to their dad's old horse-drawn machinery that their mother hated, Turpentine Day. Their dad would bring turpentine oil home in five-gallon steel cans and have the boys spread it over the wood on all the old horse-drawn equipment every summer. Even the steel horse-drawn sickle mower had a wooden tongue that required turpentine oil. The brothers would be covered in turpentine oil from head to foot when they were done. They weren't allowed into the house until they had taken a bath in a galvanized tub placed outside the ranch house and clean clothes put on. Shoes were left outside. Even then the sweet pungent smell of turpentine oil permeated the house for weeks afterwards.

One summer day the brothers talked cousins Danny and Dennis, who had come with their parents to the ranch for a week and were leaving the next day, into helping them spread turpentine oil over the old machinery. Uncle Ricardo and Aunt Anna were not very happy when they went back to Minneapolis because they had to travel the entire trip home with all four windows in their car wide open.

The brothers' favorite chore was working cattle, mostly because it required using saddle horses. They moved cattle between pastures, scattered bulls during breeding season, checked cows and caught sick calves, monitored the ranch's numerous water sources, plus checked the pasture perimeter fences on and off all summer on horseback.

A neighbor named Stanley who kept a small herd of brood mares took notice of the brothers' horsemanship skills and would bring his green, broke, two-year-old horses over for them to ride and train for him. Stanley raised sheep, and for the brothers' labor he would give them his bum lambs from spring lambing. The boys hated the lambs because they followed them everywhere bleating constantly, and their care required a lot of time.

The lambs usually went to town to be sold as soon as possible. They never sold for much, and the boys wound up being cheap labor for Stanley. The main reason they allowed Stanley to take advantage of them was his horses. Stanley knew horses and they always commanded top dollar at the monthly horse sale held in a larger town located 30 miles from the ranch. They were a pleasure to ride and train.

After a few summers of Stanley's arrangement, John and Jay devised a plan to make some real money while doing something they really enjoyed, riding horses. Jake rode and used horses, but he did not have the same passion for them as John and Jay and opted out of the endeavor. They ran the plan by their dad, and to their surprise, he agreed. If it started to interfere with their chores, though, the horses would swiftly be on their way to town.

Their plan was to attend the monthly horse sale held in town and buy two-year-old stud horses that had been rounded up on a nearby Indian reservation which could be purchased for a reasonable price. They would bring them home, geld them, and improve their condition by feeding them properly. Then they would break them into usable ranch horses and sell them for big dollars.

The reservation horses turned out to be a lot more work than they expected. To begin with, some of them had never seen a human until recently and were extremely wild. It was nothing like working with Stanley's horses.

John and Jay bought four of the reservation horses. Between their ranch duties and working with the horses, they barely had time to sleep. After about a year, they finally had the reservation horses looking decent and trained well enough for them to be taken to town and sold. John and Jay took turns riding the horses into the sales ring, demonstrating each horse's training and disposition.

The horses sold well enough but not as high as John and Jay had expected. Jay was flabbergasted. "Don't they know how much work we've put into them? We'll be lucky to break even after we pay Dad for all the feed." John agreed and that was the end of their first get-rich-quick scheme.

Occasionally during the summer, the brothers' dad would give them a Sunday afternoon off to go to a small town located eight miles northeast of the ranch. They would ride their saddle horses when they were younger and drive the ranch pickup on county gravel roads to the town when they became older. John began driving the pickup to town when he was 12.

During the summer, the town would feature a free movie every Sunday afternoon at their community hall. Community residents would sell popcorn, candy, and pop at the entrance. Everyone was required to purchase something to attend the movie.

There was a huge town park located next to the hall, and families from around the community would gather at the park, sitting in the shade of cottonwood trees eating picnic lunches. The men and boys would pitch horseshoes or play games of softball. The women would visit and relax for the day. Girls would also play softball, pitch horseshoes with the boys, play hide-and-seek, or just spend time relaxing and visiting.

The only business open in the town on Sunday was a restaurant run by a very large widow and her two equally large daughters. They always sold a lot of homemade pies and ice cream on Sundays, and if you wanted to eat, the food was also great. You had to be very careful because the owner and her daughters were always grouchy. Any one of them would not hesitate to pick a youngster up by the ears and throw them out into the street if they didn't like their attitude or behavior.

On the outskirts of the small community was a nearby lake that had been built during the Depression years by the CCC (Civilian Conservation Corps). The lake featured a sand beach. The sand was hauled in every spring and spread over the beach area by volunteers from the community. There was a lifeguard stand in the center of the beach, and every Sunday a local resident who could swim would volunteer to be the lifeguard. The beach also had a rock bath house with one bathroom that featured an ice cold shower and an area for changing into swimsuits. The bath house was shared by both girls and boys. If a girl was standing at the entrance, it meant girls only, and if a boy was standing there, it meant boys only.

Clothes would be scattered around in piles on the rock benches along the interior walls where there was always someone looking for a piece of clothing. People always checked shoes before putting them on because they never knew what someone might have put inside them.

The main attraction of the beach for the brothers was girls in swimsuits. The brothers, especially Jay, would have gone swimming at the beach every Sunday throughout the summer just for that if he could have.

UNDER FIRE

Nobody told me it would be like this

That seconds could stretch into hours

And mere minutes would seem like days

Ninety days in country seemed like forever

Two hundred seventy-five left an eternity

CHAPTER 4
Boys

The brothers grew up fast, at least that is what it seemed like to their mother. Their dad had them doing things and operating machinery well before Helen thought they could accomplish such adult functions. They were amazing at adapting to the situations and the physical requirements required to perform some of the duties.

Helen had seen John, the oldest and strongest, riding the old dump rake using both hands and bracing both feet to raise the tines up to dump the hay, an operation that an adult would perform with one hand. The boys did it all the time. Somehow, someway, they persisted, adapted, and completed the chore at hand.

A lot of the things they did scared her, but the boys seemed to enjoy the challenges. There were bumps, bruises, cuts, and sprains suffered almost daily, but they seemed to hardly notice. Helen even tried to make them take a box of bandages along, but they just stashed it in the yard and left without it. When she caught them one day and asked what was wrong with taking the box with them, they all cried out "It just gets in the way!"

The three brothers were constantly getting thrown off their horses, dragged around or run over by cattle they had roped, and cut up by fences. Machinery caused a lot of bruises, and then there was their youthful play. Everything they played had to include violent impact, usually at breakneck speed.

Helen was continually amazed that not one of the boys ever suffered a broken bone growing up. She concluded they must have some iron in them or maybe it was the Irish blood that coursed through their young veins from their dad. Or was it just luck? She never did figure it out but was glad at the end of every day that she only had to treat minor injuries.

The brothers were rambunctious but always well-mannered, and they followed instructions fairly well. They would try to bend the rules sometimes, but when they were caught, they took the punishment stoically and usually never repeated the infraction. Of the three, Jay might have been the most challenging, and Helen and Joe had to keep a closer eye on him than John or Jake.

Helen sometimes became concerned when she thought about the environment in which her boys were growing up. Some animal was always breeding another animal in front of them. Young and old livestock and wildlife were continually dying from a disease, accident, or being shot in their presence.

As they grew older, though, the brothers all began to exhibit a deep respect and compassion for the animals under their care and the wild animals around them and this made Helen worry less. The brothers also exhibited a deep respect and courteous nature toward girls, but Helen knew Jay would be the first one to discover girls. He just had a personality that drew interest from the opposite sex even as a young boy.

Helen hadn't been around hunting and trapping growing up. It just wasn't something her father did. Her family had weapons present, but they were only used occasionally to dispatch livestock for butchering and occasional varmints, so hunting and harvesting wild game was something she had to adapt to. She became amazed at the income the boys made from hunting and trapping and was grateful for it, plus it kept them busy.

The brothers did have quiet moments which Helen enjoyed immensely. When they were younger, they would gather around the huge wooden radio eating popcorn she had prepared. They didn't make a sound except for the crunching of popcorn as they listened to a *Hopalong Cassidy* or *The Lone Ranger* program. After the program, the action would begin with cap guns snapping continuously as they reenacted the television program.

Jake, the youngest, was eight years old when

they finally got a TV. It was a huge contraption with a screen that projected black and white images only, and it completely mesmerized the brothers, especially after they were able to view their first western. The TV was used sparingly, playing westerns for the boys and comedy programs for Helen and Joe, plus the nightly news program. They only had access to one local station, and the news program featured one announcer who covered the local, regional, and national news, then he presented the local and regional weather, and finally, he covered local and regional sports.

One day they were in town and stopped at the Dairy Queen for an ice cream treat. The brothers had earned the treat for helping Helen complete household chores. While they were there, the announcer from television came into the Dairy Queen, and the brothers were in awe seeing an actual person they'd seen on their TV in person.

Helen found herself purchasing hydrogen peroxide and bandages by the case instead of individually, and she always made sure to have gauze, compress wraps, and other medical supplies on hand. One day she had to make a quick trip into town for some needed baler parts. She was dressed in her haying clothes, with dust and dirt present all over her, and she stopped at the local drug store to pick up her usual cache of medical supplies.

The pharmacist's wife who was assisting her said, "Oh Helen, I just don't know how you can do it, raising three boys while helping out with field work, making hay all summer!"

Helen answered, "The boys keep me busy, but they are manageable with some discipline, but sometimes it's Joe who concerns me. Like just this morning when I was expressing some concerns about keeping track of the boys, he said, 'Raising boys is easy, just tie them to Bubba and he will take care of them, guaranteed.' Now what kind of a train of thought is that?"

They both laughed as the pharmacist's wife said, "Men! How can you possibly understand them?"

Bubba was the family dog who accompanied the brothers everywhere except when they went hunting, when he was secured on a long leash with water, food. and shade near his doghouse. Bubba was an Australian Shepherd their dad purchased from a rancher who lived about 80 miles south of them. The rancher raised registered Polled Herford cattle and sold bulls to local ranchers and registered heifers to other registered breeders. He also raised registered Suffolk sheep and sold breeding rams and ewes to area sheep producers. Along with the Herford cattle and Suffolk sheep, he raised registered Australian Shepherds and sold registered pups. The dogs were what their dad was interested in. He bought a couple of bulls now and then, but primarily he wanted the breeder's Australian Shepherd dogs because of their temperament and intelligence.

Someone in the neighborhood was usually trying to give pups away, and their dad had tried a free pup many times. Because of inbreeding and the constant infusion of different breeds being mixed randomly, they usually turned out to be more of a nuisance and sometimes even dangerous, requiring him to take them on one last trip over the hill.

Being a ranch dog was hard on a dog because of the hazards they were constantly exposed to from cattle, horses, wildlife, machinery, and vehicles. It took a good dog to survive for very long on a ranch. When the current ranch dog was lost due to an accident, their dad would write his rancher friend and make another 80-mile trip to secure another Bubba. The only dog's name the brothers knew was Bubba. It was the only name their dad would allow the current ranch dog to be named.

The brothers grew up fast and all had inherited some of their dad's distinct Irish features and thick, light-brown hair. When Helen saw all of them together, she would sometimes step back and be somewhat amazed at what a handsome trio the boys made alongside their dad. Helen thought Joe was the handsomest man she had ever met.

They definitely looked like brothers. They had all become taller than their dad who was almost six feet tall. John and Jake were both six feet three inches tall, and Jay was exactly six feet. Their mother thought being the shortest was what made him the most rambunctious of her sons. They were all well-built and exhibited a muscular prowess and agility that was above average for their age. It didn't really surprise her. She knew how hard they worked and how much they ate every day.

Helen was totally amazed at how much food the three of them consumed. She was a petite, striking woman of German descent with a slight olive complexion and thick black hair.

At times, she would become embarrassed with the amount of groceries she had to purchase at the local grocery store because of the expressions the store owner or his employees sometimes gave her. "What could you possibly be doing with all this food? Feeding an army, or what?"

So, one day she made all three of her sons come with her to purchase groceries. When the store owner and his employees saw the boys grown up, they immediately realized where all the groceries were going. After that, they went out of their way to assist Helen. She had heard Joe tell the boys one day that perception is 85 percent visual, and boy, was he right!

Hunting and trapping became the brothers' primary pastime. They loved all the challenges, not only those presented by the game they were hunting but also the weather conditions which they were subjected to. The boys were proud of being able to outsmart and outwit wildlife, whose senses were far greater than those of humans. It was also great that they were getting paid for something they loved doing.

Trapping began in the fall after wildlife had primed up or acquired their winter fur, and it continued through early spring. Coyotes, fox, badger, raccoons, beaver, mink, weasel, muskrats, and the occasional skunk were the primary furbearers that they trapped. Jackrabbits and cottontail rabbits were hunted with rifles and shotguns primarily by walk-up hunting, which was walking into likely areas and jump shooting them when they broke cover.

Coyotes and fox were also hunted with varmint calls. The brothers became quite adept at calling with mouth calls but switched to cassette tapes when cassette players came out because of the greater volume. They took a two-foot by two-foot piece of plywood and mounted a cassette player with an external speaker beside it onto the plywood, attached a carrying handle, and used it quite extensively. The downfall was that the entire setup was heavy and required spare batteries in extremely cold weather. The cassette tapes were also susceptible to cold, so the batteries and cassette tapes were carried in pullover vests with carrying pockets sewn on by their mother. The vests were worn under coats to use body heat to keep everything warm and operational.

In the spring before the ice broke up, the river was in its annual spring flood stage, often running bank full. The brothers would put a canoe in the river and float downstream with the current, shooting any beaver who were out of their dens up on the banks escaping the flood waters.

Floating a flooding river was always a challenging adventure, so the flooding river was monitored daily. The boys waited for the initial rush of water to subside and the current to slow down slightly, then they had to get out into the river before the ice began to break up. Floating ice would have made being on the river too dangerous. They used an old Remington 572 pump action tubular feed rimfire rifle for shooting beaver from the canoe. It was tied to the canoe with a piece of light rope in case it got dropped overboard. Hunting beaver from a canoe in a flooding river was dangerous but usually very productive, and the brothers would be busy afterwards skinning, stretching, scraping, and sewing up bullet holes sometimes late into the evening.

The brothers also hunted pheasants, partridge, and especially sharp-tail grouse whose numbers were astronomical due to a government program called Soil Bank. That program paid farmers to seed cropland to grass for 10 years. The grass could only be cut for hay if approved because of drought for emergency hay supplies.

After they became old enough to qualify for licenses, they hunted deer and antelope. Helen prepared the wild game for them but never liked the smell and taste herself. It was a learning experience because wild game meat required different techniques, and she failed a lot at first. A neighbor lady whose family hunted a lot took Helen under her wing and taught her how to prepare the wild game, and she also shared recipes with Helen.

Helen was particular about what the brothers brought in for her to prepare—no bloody or bruised meat was allowed. Also, no hair or fat could be left on the meat. They always complied with her wishes and complimented her.

They even talked their mom into preparing a couple of snapping turtles one summer. They had read an article with instructions for preparing turtles for consumption in the monthly *Fur-Fish-Game* magazine that they subscribed to. She prepared the turtles once, then she informed them if they wanted turtles again, the kitchen was all theirs. They even kept some beaver meat and ground it up into hamburger, an idea they got from another article in the magazine, and grilled it outside on a grill. It tasted like cardboard, and that was the end of beaver burgers.

All income and expenses were split equally between the three brothers. There was never any squabbling. Even if you did not make the shot or set the trap, they were all there and had struggled just as much as the others. It was the brothers' bond and mutual agreement that was special.

Their dad, who noticed everything, was silently proud to see their teamwork and bonding, plus all the extraordinary skills his sons were exhibiting. He knew his boys would be ready to fight for their country if called upon.

MOMENTS

War is a collection of moments

Get through the moment and live to wake
another day

If you didn't survive the moment, you went
home ahead of schedule

And the moments became nonexistent

CHAPTER 5
Cousins

On their dad's side of the family, the brothers only had two cousins. Joe's only brother had died while serving in World War II, and his only sister, who was much older, lived in Canada with her husband and two children.

The brothers were able to meet their two older Canadian cousins once when they took a trip to Canada. Their dad's sister and her husband started coming down every summer from Canada after they were both retired until they were unable to travel. Their two children, who were much older than the brothers, never did make a trip down to the ranch.

Helen's parents had sold their farm and moved to Arizona permanently shortly after their youngest daughter graduated from high school. Because Helen's parents made only one annual summer trip, the brothers saw their surviving grandparents when their turn for a visit came, but they stayed in constant contact with them by mail.

Helen's five sisters all lived out of state in cities. Every summer the brothers looked forward to their mother's sisters and their families coming to the ranch. They always stayed for at least a week, and the visits usually coincided with certain summer activities that each sister enjoyed.

The cousins were all city slickers who knew nothing about ranch life, and the brothers enjoyed indoctrinating them into their world. The work didn't stop just because cousins were visiting, and the cousins usually participated in whatever ranch duties were being performed. They usually left the ranch bruised, sore, and sporting bandages. On one occasion, a cousin left with a broken arm.

During specific wild berry harvesting periods, Aunt Beatrice, her husband, Henry, along with their children, Buddy and Bridget, visited the ranch. They were joined by Aunt Betty, whose husband had died in World War II, and her son, Calvin, from Chicago. The harvesting periods were June for juneberries, August for chokecherries, and occasionally September for buffalo berries and plums. The relatives would turn the kitchen into a factory for a couple of days processing the berries into jams and pie fillings, and they'd leave with a trunk full of processed wild berry products.

Aunt Betty worked on the production line in an Allis-Chalmers tractor factory in Chicago. She was always trying to convince Joe to switch from

John Deere tractors to Allis-Chalmers tractors. One day after listening to her pitch, he replied. "I would consider an Allis-Chalmers tractor if they changed colors. It would feel like I was riding around on an orange all day and I don't like oranges!"

The Allis-Chalmers company had chosen a dull orange paint color for tractors and other farming equipment that was manufactured in their Chicago plant. Aunt Betty was flabbergasted and asked Joe if he had bumped his head earlier in the day.

Joe replied, "Not that I can recollect!"

Aunt Betty put her hands on her hips and responded, "A bump on the head is not going to stop me. I will just wait until you get your senses back."

Aunt Eustis and her husband, George, came to the ranch from Minneapolis in August for chicken butchering. They brought their three children, Clifford, and the twins, Sandy and Susan. Aunt Eustis loved butchering chickens, and Helen appreciated the help. She always sent her sister home with a trunk full of frozen chickens. Aunt Eustis would make Clifford, Sandy, and Susan help with the butchering, and Helen would make the brothers help too.

The brothers enjoyed eating the processed product, just not the butchering. One summer they came up with a plan to get out of having to help butcher chickens. The morning of chicken butchering day while they were still in the house having breakfast, a neighbor's son, Jerry, called. He asked Helen if the brothers could come over and help him break up a bull fight between their bull and one of the O'Janon's. After that, they would need to separate cows and calves from the two herds that had become mixed together after the bulls had torn down the fence line, and then help repair the fence. Joe and George had run into town for urgent business, something they seemed to do every chicken butchering day.

Helen was not happy, but on a ranch, cows usually came first. John and Jay saddled horses. Jake loaded the pickup with wire, fence posts, and fencing tools plus lunch, and they headed north to the pasture where the cows were located. Jerry, the neighbor who had called them, was waiting at the pasture gate. Jake drove the pickup and Jerry, John, and Jay rode their horses down into a draw with a live spring that was used to water the cattle. They hobbled the horses and laid back in the shade of a giant boxelder tree visiting, eating, and taking naps.

Later that afternoon when Joe and George got home, Joe was surprised to see that Helen, Eustis, Clifford, Sandy, and Susan were still butchering chickens. Then he noticed that the boys were gone. When he asked Helen, she told him of the issue with the bulls and that the boys had left right after breakfast to help Jerry get the bulls, cows, and calves separated, and they had been gone most of the day.

Joe immediately saddled a horse and headed north. He found them asleep under the boxelder tree and woke them with his usual dialogue, "What do you boys think this is, a laying around joint!"

The brothers and Jerry were startled, and they all had the look of guilty puppies caught in the act of something mischievous. All Joe could do was laugh and shake his head. Then he said, "I'll cover for you boys this time, but if you ever try something like this again on your mother, I'll tell her the whole story, and you boys will be sleeping in the doghouse eating dry bread for months."

Aunt Katherine and her daughters, Debbie and Paulette, from Billings, Montana, always came during haying season. Aunt Katherine's husband, Stanley, was a long-haul trucker who took one vacation a year over Christmas, so the brothers rarely got to see him. Aunt Katherine loved haying and came every summer to help Joe and the brothers mow, rake, and bale hay. She was very adept at operating haying equipment and would keep at it until it was too dark to see. Debbie and Paulette stayed around the yard and helped Helen with housework and gardening. Aunt Katherine always hated to leave because there was usually more haying to do.

Aunt Anna, her husband, Ricardo, and their boys, Danny and Dennis from Minneapolis came during grain harvest because Ricardo liked helping combine grain. If Joe did not have any grain to harvest, Ricardo would go over and help neighbors harvest their grain. His favorite harvesting job was hauling grain to the elevator in town and mingling with the farmers while waiting in line to dump the grain on his truck. The brothers thought Uncle Ricardo had a loose screw somewhere in his head, but he was an interesting man, and everyone liked the little Italian guy.

One summer their dad had purchased a new horse. It was a well-built bay gelding who was good at handling cattle, but he had one issue that their dad hadn't taken the time to break him of yet. The bay would stand perfectly still while you put a foot into a stirrup and grabbed the saddle horn, but as soon as you started to swing up into the saddle, he would start spinning violently in a circle and would not stop until you were in the saddle.

Aunt Anna, Uncle Ricardo, and Danny were on vacation and staying at the ranch for a week. Dennis had stayed home with Ricardo's sister to complete a summer school program he was required to take to pass onto the next grade.

Danny was an older first cousin who would try to bully the brothers but only when no adults were around. The brothers as a unit were usually able to hold their ground, but after a week, they would grow tired of Danny.

One day the brothers invited Danny to take a ride on the new horse. Danny was mean and abusive to horses while riding them, and he instantly jumped at the opportunity to bully a new horse. The bay was saddled and placed near the barn. Danny was not informed of the spinning issue, and when he started to swing up into the saddle, the bay went into his usual violent spin. Danny lost his grip and went flying face-first into the side of the barn, his arms and legs splayed out forming a perfect "X" on the barn wall.

The brothers started laughing so hard that they could barely stand. Danny just kind of melted off the barn wall onto the ground, slumped over, and didn't move. The brothers' demeanor quickly changed to panic as they all thought the same thing. They'd killed him!

Danny eventually started to move and tried to stand, but all he could manage was to get up onto his hands and knees. His nose was bleeding profusely, and he had trouble speaking, but at least he was alive.

After that day Danny refused any opportunity to ride a horse while visiting the ranch. The brothers' plan had worked, and the trouble they got into for riding the new horse without permission was well worth it. They could also tell their dad was pleased even though he tried not to show it.

Another summer their dad had broken up some hay land and decided to plant wheat into the field the first year before reseeding it back into hay. It was a very dry spring, and after the field was planted, the only thing that came up was a whole field of thistles. To stop the thistles from spreading, their dad mowed the field and then hooked up a B John Deere tractor to the dump rake and had two of the boys, one on the tractor and one on the dump rake, make windrows of thistles so they could be burned.

Staying on the dump rake was a challenge. It ran on steel wheels and had a small steel seat mounted in the center with a hand lever next to it that required manual operation to raise the rake's tines to dump the accumulated thistles. For the boys it required the use of both hands while bracing both feet against the rake's frame to raise the rake tines. This was accomplished while the tractor and rake were in motion moving forward. Riding the dump rake was John's responsibility because he was the oldest and strongest of the brothers. Jay and Jake took turns driving the B John Deere tractor.

Aunt Beatrice and Aunt Betty along with Buddy and Bridget came to the ranch for wild berry picking while the boys were raking up the thistles to burn, and their cousin Buddy thought it would be neat to ride the dump rake one afternoon. John was tired and needed a break, so he gave the seat to Buddy and showed him how to operate the hand lever with instructions when to dump the thistles. John then sat down in the shade of the pickup with a one-gallon glass jug wrapped in burlap that had been filled with water earlier that morning and watched Jay and Buddy disappear over a small rise in the field. When he spotted them again, Buddy was gone from sight.

John jumped into the pickup and followed their path to find Buddy, but he could not spot him anywhere. He ran down Jay, who hadn't looked back for a while and had no idea where Buddy was. They eventually heard him hollering from inside the thistles, rolled up under the dump rake's tines. When they finally got him dug out, they had never seen anyone as scratched up as Buddy was. His shirt was torn to pieces, and he had lost his wallet, which they never did find.

Buddy came back out to the field a couple of days later because he thought burning the thistles would be fun. He burned off his eyebrows all on his own and really did look bad when they left for home a few days later. His face and arms were severely scratched up, with bandages scattered here and there, and he had no eyebrows. Helen had a talk with the brothers about their behavior with poor cousin Buddy, and she was worried he might never visit them again. They didn't say it, but Buddy just wasn't their favorite cousin.

Their cousin Clifford from Minneapolis was a real city slicker, small in stature, who didn't like getting dirty and was always dressed in fancy clothes. One day the brothers and some neighborhood friends invited him to play King of the Hill on a stack of baled hay.

King of the Hill was a favorite game of the brothers and neighboring boys. To begin the game, straws were drawn, and whoever drew the long straw climbed to the top of a stack of bales. The other boys would wait until he got to the top and then mob him from all four sides and try to throw, shove, or push him off the stack and then turn on each other. Once you hit the ground, you had to stay there until everyone had been thrown off the stack except one person, who then became the King of the Hill.

Clifford did not have a clue what he was getting into. The brothers had rigged it so all the straws were long, and being the guest, Cllifford was allowed to draw first. When they saw that it was a long straw, the drawing was stopped. Clifford was then congratulated for drawing the long straw and directed to climb to the top of the stack. He was beaming when he reached the top and seemed to enjoy his stature as the King of the Hill.

The utopia didn't last long when a screaming mob of young boys surrounded the stack and began ascending toward him, pushing and shoving each other on the way up. Clifford panicked and began running along the top of the stack and took a giant leap into the air when he reached the end of the stack. He landed on a fence post which broke his arm.

Their mother was not very happy and forbid them from ever playing the game again, but they couldn't stop. They just moved to haystacks farther away from the ranch. Their dad knew what they were up to, and he took them to the stack where Clifford had broken his arm and had them explain the event. He just stood there shaking his head without saying a word. The brothers knew he was thinking about what an idiot anyone would have to be to make a jump like Clifford had.

Joe gave them instructions to never play the game again with city cousins and to always clean up the stack immediately when they were done. The brothers were relieved because they thought they were going to be disciplined. Instead, they kind of received permission from their dad to keep playing, something they would never reveal to their mother if she caught them playing King of the Hill.

The brothers all began twirling ropes early in life and went through a roping stage where anything was fair game. They were not allowed to rope any of the calves kept around the ranch because their dad didn't want them running off pounds that were costing money to put on. They would rope each other and try to rope Bubba, cats, stray chickens, and anything else that moved.

One Sunday morning, Helen and Aunt Eustis dressed up the twins, Sandy and Susan, in dresses and took them to church. Their error was not making the twins change immediately after they got home. When the girls came outside to play, the brothers talked them into pretending they were calves they would try to rope.

Sandy and Susan soon grew tired of the game and went inside to find something else to do. When

Helen and Aunt Eustis saw them, they were almost in shock. The dresses were completely soiled and even torn in places. When they asked the girls what had happened, they explained the game they had been playing with the boys.

Helen marched outside, had a serious talk with the brothers, and took the ropes away from them. She told them their dad would determine the punishment when he got home, and they were not allowed to rope anyone or anything until Aunt Eustis left.

Their cousin Dennis from Minneapolis was a nice guy but just not the brightest person and extremely naive. He would fall for every prank they could come up with and then fall for another one the very next day. Joe didn't farm much, but when he did, it was the brothers' responsibility to get an old John Deere pull type combine ready to harvest whatever grain had been planted.

Dennis and his parents just happened to be visiting and another prank was devised. Dennis's help was requested to get the combine, which was parked in a hay yard near the ranch, ready for the harvest.

They began by checking all fluids and replacing or filling them to the proper levels. They greased and checked all bearings, installed the necessary drive chains and belts, and crawled into and under the combine checking for excessive wear spots that would require welding. Then they produced a hand air pump that was used for minor needs around the ranch, hooked it up to one of the large tires located on either side of the combine that carried the entire weight of the machine, and began pumping. Dennis couldn't believe that they were going to fill a giant tire like that with a hand pump. The brothers told him that the hand pump was all they had, and this was how they filled the tires every year.

They took turns pumping for most of the afternoon, checking the tire's pressure periodically. It was hard work, and Dennis took his turn not wanting to be outdone by any of the brothers. Near the end of the day when the proper pressure was finally reached, the brothers could see that Dennis was done and would not be able to continue so they took him back to the yard. He immediately went into the house, fell asleep, and slept straight through until the next morning.

Dennis was clearly in pain and could barely raise his arms to eat breakfast, but he followed the brothers outside to help them with the combine which had been pulled up to the ranch shop early that morning. When they pulled an electric air compressor from the shop and filled the other tire with air in minutes, Dennis was very agitated, but true to form, he fell for another prank the very next day.

One spring a neighbor decided to buy a semi load of Holstein pail calves from Minnesota. He didn't want the whole load, but the deal was a whole load or nothing, so he ran around the neighborhood looking for partners. Joe decided to take a dozen or so of the pail calves and throw them in with the five bum calves in the corral from calving. The brothers wound up with 20 pail calves that they had to feed milk replacer to twice a day. They would pen up 10 calves at a time, mix up ten buckets of milk replacer with water, and hook the pails on a fence line and turn a mob of 10 calves loose to drink milk. They had to monitor the calves so they wouldn't spill their milk or steal another calf's milk. It was always a ruckus.

Aunt Katherine and Debbie and Paulette were visiting during the beginning of haying season. The pail calves were older and just about ready to be switched to dry feed from the milk replacer, and the brothers came up with a plan to have some fun with the girls.

One morning they invited them to help feed the pail calves. Debbie and Paulette were excited and helped separate the calves into groups of 10 and mix up the milk replacer. The brothers then had them crawl over the fence and handed them each two pails full of milk replacer and told them to pick out four calves to feed. Then they opened the gate and let 10 calves into the pen.

The calves rushed at Debbie and Paulette. Debbie's milk wound up spilling all over her T-shirt. Paulette was luckier, and her milk spilled onto the ground. The calves knocked Debbie over and started sucking on her milk-soaked T-shirt and eventually pulled it off her. Paulette ran to the fence and vaulted over it.

The brothers were laughing as they crawled in the pen to help Debbie. They were able to get her out from underneath the calves and retrieve what little was left of her T-shirt. They handed it to her and turned their backs so she could put it on. That was a big mistake, because after pulling her T-shirt back on, Debbie grabbed a pail and managed to give John, Jay, and Jake a good beating before they were able to jump the fence and get away from her. They all agreed after the event that the lumps were well worth it.

The most serious issue the brothers ever got into with a cousin was when they were very young and Calvin, who was much older, had talked them into going on a camping trip up in the hip-roofed barn's hayloft. Everything was going along great. They had made up comfortable beds using hay from within the loft and were going to have a camp lunch with items they had sneaked out of the house. Calvin insisted that they needed a campfire, so he had the brothers gather up pieces of wood from around the barnyard which he stacked up like a tepee on the loft floor with a small amount of hay in the center.

Calvin then brought out a box of matches that he had sneaked out of the kitchen and lit the campfire. Even though they were very young and had never been around a campfire, they knew something was not right and tried to stop Calvin. He pushed them back and accidentally kicked the burning wood and hay over into hay that was stacked in the barn's loft. The fire suddenly expanded and engulfed the entire hayloft in searing heat and flames.

They all escaped by jumping out of the open hayloft door. They were sore and bruised but had escaped the fire. All the brothers could do was stand and watch the barn burn and wait for their punishment. The barn was a total loss, and all that remained were the concrete footings which outlined where it used to be.

After their story, the punishment that they had expected was never administered. They were given a stern lecture by their mom and dad about matches and instructed to never allow city cousins access to them when they were on the ranch. Calvin never came back to the ranch after that day, but Aunt Betty came with Aunt Beatrice every summer for wild berry picking and processing.

Even though the brothers sometimes got into trouble because of cousins, their visits were always a welcome break from the monotony of working on the ranch every day from sunup to sundown for the entire summer.

DOGS OF WAR

Young boys going to war

Trained to believe we were invincible

After the reality of combat

Survival became our only goal

As we became dogs of war

CHAPTER 6
Uncle Hugo

The brothers' favorite neighbor was an old Swede bachelor who lived north of the ranch about five miles in an area called The Little Badlands. They called him Uncle Hugo even though he wasn't related. He was a huge man with sharp Nordic features and hands as big as plates. Uncle Hugo had left his family and home in Sweden to escape a life of working underground in the coal mines. He was grateful for every day spent outdoors working with his livestock and crops and was always in a jolly mood.

Uncle Hugo lived in a one-room sod house, and the boys thought it was the neatest place in the world. Numerous mice also thought it was a great place, and the sod walls were home to scores of them. Uncle Hugo kept a loaded 22 rimfire revolver on the table and would grab it and shoot mice as they presented themselves within the interior walls of the house. He also encouraged the boys to do the same though their marksmanship wasn't near his level, even when they used a huge sugar shaker on the table for a pistol rest.

The boys wanted to live just like Uncle Hugo did, but they began to have doubts. One day, after a hard day's labor, Uncle Hugo invited them in for some of his famous stew before taking them home. There was always a huge pot of stew simmering on the stove, and it was always good until that day.

As he began to dish up stew for the boys, he said something curtly in Swedish, reached into the pot, and pulled a dead sparrow out of the stew and flung it out the nearest window. After getting rid of the sparrow, Uncle Hugo dished up huge portions of the stew for the boys which they reluctantly consumed because they knew they would not be allowed to leave until they had finished it.

Uncle Hugo told the brothers, "Never waste food. It's too hard to come by."

After that day the boys always tried to avoid eating stew at Uncle Hugo's, but he always insisted, and they always complied.

The sod home had two windows and one door without any screens on them, and they were all kept open in the summer and closed in the winter. Wildlife could come and go at will. One day when they entered his house, the entire table was covered with newspapers. When they asked what the newspapers were for, Uncle Hugo pointed up to a barn swallow nest in the rafters just above the table. He stood there for a while looking up at the nest, let out a sigh, and said, "I'm not going to disrupt them from raising their young. But I don't like bird droppings all over my table, so I just change the newspapers when I sit down to eat. Let this be a lesson for you boys—that man and wildlife can live together. You just have to adapt a little now and then."

The brothers never told their mother for she would not have let them ever go over there again. As a matter of fact, they didn't tell her much of what went on over at Uncle Hugo's because it was strictly a man's world, and she wouldn't have understood.

A cloud of dust coming from the north usually meant Uncle Hugo had experienced another catastrophe and needed the boys' help immediately. Even as youngsters, they just couldn't believe some of the predicaments he could get himself into.

One fall during the grain harvesting season when their dad needed the boys' help harvesting the barley he'd planted that spring, Uncle Hugo showed up needing the boys help for another emergency that could not wait. That was the year he had purchased a new pull-type combine which was going to make his harvest much easier and more efficient.

Because he worked alone most of the time, he did things differently than the average farmer. When the grain hopper on his new combine became full, instead of augering the grain onto his truck and hauling it home or to town like everyone else did, he would auger it onto piles out in the fields to be loaded onto his truck later, and he'd keep combining until his crop was safely on piles for transport at his convenience. Everything would have been okay except he turned his cows onto the harvested fields to forage before he had hauled away any of the grain piles. He was extremely concerned because he could lose the entire herd from bloat. The boys were struggling, trying to move the cows and their calves off the grain piles onto an adjoining pasture, and if their dad and some neighbors hadn't come over to help, they probably wouldn't have gotten all the cows out alive.

Uncle Hugo was so proud of the job the boys had done to help him save his herd that he picked out a cow and gave it to them. After a short period of time, they began to wish that they had never taken the cow home because she was one catastrophe after another, just like her previous owner.

If she could not crawl through a fence, she would jump over it. Her calf was constantly running around bawling, looking for his mother because she would often just disappear, and the poor little guy was always hungry. The first time they ran her into an alley to vaccinate and pour insecticide over her back, she got her head stuck between the corral planks, and they had to take a plank off to get her head unstuck. Their dad finally had enough and hauled her to town.

Another year Uncle Hugo decided to feed the steers in his herd through the winter and then sell them in the spring. His feedlot facilities were not the greatest, but most of the steers stayed within the confines of the feedlot except for a black, white-faced steer which he had named Elmer. Elmer would wander around the yard at will and even come up to the door of the house, stick his head in, and look around.

One day that spring before Uncle Hugo had hauled the steers to town for sale, he came barreling into the yard. Elmer was in trouble, and he needed the boys' assistance. When they arrived at his yard, he led them over to an abandoned, hand-dug well that was about six feet across and 20-some feet deep, lined with stacked rock. Elmer was at the bottom, and he didn't look alive. When the boys asked how long he had been in the well, Uncle Hugo answered, "Well, I've been looking for him for a few days now."

Ropes were dropped down into the well, and John and Jay went down into the dark, wet cavern to secure Elmer with chains for removal. After they were done and had crawled back out of the well, Uncle Hugo used a tractor to pull Elmer out. Jake took one look at Elmer and said, "Wow, that is one big, dead steer for the coyotes!"

Uncle Hugo showed a side of himself that the boys had never seen. He became very emotional as he described his relationship with Elmer. Uncle

Hugo began his story, "There was a spring storm during calving last spring that began late in the afternoon. About midnight I went to check on the herd, and I found a cow out in the storm trying to calve but needing help, so I herded her into the barn and pulled the calf. I carried the calf into the house, dried him off, and put him near the stove to warm up. After he had warmed up and was trying to stand, I carried him out to the barn and put him with his anxious mother. She immediately began cleaning him with her tongue and nudging him around to help him stand so he could nurse. Boy, was he hungry! Throughout the summer, I would see him running around like calves do, playing. He was always the leader of the group, and he would follow his mother everywhere, no matter how tall or steep a hill she had decided to graze on. I named him *Elmer* after a friend that I used to play with back in the old country. Elmer was not going to town with the other steers. He was going to stay here on the farm with me. Now, you boys help me dig a hole and bury him, so he can stay here. I know the coyotes need to eat, but today, they'll just have to find something else."

The best escapade ever initiated by Uncle Hugo was the year that he had a new, one-room, wooden house built next to his old sod home. His place was in a bowl with a horseshoe-shaped hill that had gentle slopes cascading down into his yard surrounding it on three sides.

Uncle Hugo rarely bought batteries. He would

just park all his machinery and vehicles on the hill surrounding his place. To start them he would release the brakes, shift the vehicle into neutral, and give it a push to start it moving down the hill. Then he would jump in, put the vehicle in gear, and pop the clutch.

When he went to town or anyplace else, he would either park on a hill or just let the vehicle run. That fall after Uncle Hugo had delivered his last load of grain to the elevator in town, he stopped at a local bar to celebrate the completion of his harvest and probably had a little too much to drink. When he arrived at the top of the hill above his place, he exited the truck and started walking down the hill to his house only he had forgotten to put the truck in gear and set the emergency brake. The truck rolled right by him and didn't stop until it was inside his new house.

It was difficult for the brothers to keep straight faces while they helped clean up the mess and move Uncle Hugo back into the sod house for the winter. The next spring Uncle Hugo had a new, one-room cinder block house with indoor plumbing and a propane heater built beside the wrecked wooden house. This was the first time in his life that he had lived in a home with indoor plumbing. There was a sink in the kitchen that provided cold water only.

When Joe asked him why he hadn't put in a hot water heater, Uncle Hugo replied, "Them rascal plumber guys tried to talk me into one, and I told them that's what stoves are for."

There was a toilet in a back corner of his new one-room house with drapes suspended from the ceiling surrounding the toilet area for privacy. One day while the brothers were visiting and having stew again with Uncle Hugo, he excused himself from the table, got up, and went to the bathroom. The boys could hear the whole event along with some mumbling about hemorrhoids as they sat at the table trying not to laugh out loud. When Uncle Hugo was done, he flushed the toilet, pulled the drapes back, and came walking back to the table with a scowl on his face. He sat down and said, "That darn toilet cost me more than the whole house." Then the scowl on his face became a smile as he said, "And it's worth every penny. Now you boys remember that!"

It always brought a smile to the brothers' faces when they came over the hill, and there facing them, was a falling-down sod house with a wrecked wooden house next to it and then a brick house situated off to the side, all in a very neat row.

PROFILE

THREE CLASSES OF PEOPLE WENT TO VIETNAM

THE POOR

THE DISPOSED

THE PATRIOTIC

ONLY ONE CLASS CAME HOME

THE SURVIVORS

CHAPTER 7
Hunting

When the three brothers left the house to load hunting gear into the old '48 Chevy, they checked the temperature gauge which read 23 degrees below zero. They estimated that the current wind speed was at least 20 miles per hour. The weather forecast was for increasing wind speeds and temperatures to remain in the negative category for the day.

The wind chill would be around 50 degrees below zero, but Sunday was the only day the brothers had time to leave the ranch to hunt. They knew from experience that school and ranch chores would occupy the rest of their week. Hunting coyotes was a primary revenue source for the brothers, and it seemed as if they were always in need of money, so they were going hunting regardless of the weather. Besides, it was not anything that they had not been through before. They had grown up and adapted to their environment just as their prey had. Because of the wind, they would not be able to use varmint calls, their favorite and most successful method of hunting. But it was a perfect day for spot and stalk hunting.

They had bought the '48 Chevy for 50 dollars so they could hunt and trap a greater area than hunting on foot allowed them. The old car had paid for itself many times over, but it just wasn't very good in snow. The brothers' dream was getting a Willys Jeep which would give them greater access to the countryside in the winter.

Chains and scoop shovels were taken along because the rural backroads were covered with accumulated snow which would limit accessibility. Snowshoes would take over when the old Chevy gave out which wouldn't take much. It seemed like it had snowed every other day for a month, and when it wasn't snowing, the wind blew the accumulated snow at will into great drifts blocking backroads until the spring thaw.

The old '48 Chevy had just barely made it through a snow-laden backroad, and the brothers stopped to survey the next passage when Jay burst out, "Coyotes up on Lone Butte about three quarters of the way up! It looks like a convention!"

Even though the pack was over a mile away, the brothers knew they had been seen by the pack. Any attempt to make a move from their present location would be in vain, so they turned around and exited the area. They never even had to speak about it. They had been hunting together for so long that each one knew what needed to be done to make the hunt successful.

After driving back about a mile, they pulled over and began preparing to move in on the coyotes. They knew it would be a long, hard hike to reach Lone Butte, but before they had attained transportation, they used to hike all day through variable weather conditions in pursuit of coyotes. This jaunt wasn't viewed as too great a challenge.

Each one grabbed a rifle. Jake's weapon was a Marlin lever action 22 rimfire rifle with open sights which belonged to their dad. Jay used an old sporterized Mauser 30-06 with peep sights given to the brothers by their friend Uncle Carl. John carried their pride and joy, a Remington Model 722 chambered-in 222 which had a four-power Weaver scope mounted on it for greater accuracy. It was not the perfect arsenal for hunting coyotes, but it was all they had, and a lot of game had been taken with the three rifles.

They also carried two pairs of binoculars, and for camouflage they had modified old white sheets into pullover ponchos. The brothers were serious about coyote hunting. They just did not have the revenue to outfit themselves properly, but they made do with what they had until they could afford better equipment.

Jake took point. Even though he was the youngest, he was the best stalker of the brothers. He seemed to possess a sixth sense that always put them in the right place at the right time, and this was serious business. The brothers were excited because of the number of coyotes gathered up in one pack. If they could pull this stalk off successfully, it would be like getting paid and then getting a bonus.

If John or Jay disagreed with Jake's route, they would communicate by hand signals only. No words would be spoken until the stalk was over. Noise and movement were the primary concern. They did not want to accidentally startle a deer, rabbit, grouse, or any other animal on their route of travel. That would alert the very perceptive coyotes who would not delay a hasty exit before they could precisely identify the cause of anything out of the ordinary.

Jake was in no hurry and exhibited extreme caution even early in the stalk. You never knew what could happen, and he knew that his brothers were depending on him just as he would be depending on them to make good clean shots once they were in position. The old, accumulated snow had been recently covered with a fresh layer of snow which helped muffle the sound of their footsteps. Every rise was skirted carefully to avoid sky lining, and they stopped frequently to scan the terrain and adjust the route of travel to gain every advantage available. The wind was constantly checked during the stalk.

The coyotes were on the south slope of Lone Butte in a swale which protected them from the cold, northwest wind while allowing them to soak up what little heat the sun projected through the cold air blanket covering their world during the winter months. The location afforded them excellent visibility while extremely sensitive noses and hearing protected them from any danger behind them. They were in a perfect location, and it was up to the brothers to penetrate the wall of security without being detected.

Jake had decided to go directly over the top of Lone Butte, but Jay stopped him. Through hand signals, he directed Jake to lead them to an adjoining butte from which they would make the final assault. John was always amazed at how well his two younger brothers functioned as a team. There was never any hesitation to accept an alternate plan or route if it made sense.

This new plan made sense, except for the distance, which would make Jake's 22 unacceptable for shooting. But Jake knew his brothers could shoot and that his plan would give them only moving targets. Jay's plan would give them at least two stationary shots, and if the coyotes moved right, he could even get in on the action.

The boys' movements were slow and arduous once they reached the adjoining butte. The stalk worked beautifully. They were able to shoot three coyotes from Lone Butte. John and Jay had both made their stationary shots, and Jay shot another coyote on the run using the old Mauser with peep sights. On the hike back to the Chevy, John also shot another coyote that was out hunting alone and had not detected them soon enough.

It had turned out to be one of those memorable hunts despite the extreme weather conditions, with four coyotes to show for their efforts. To them it felt as if it could not have been any better.

While they were driving back to the ranch, Jake suddenly bellowed out, "You boys are crazy if you think you're going to get anything in this weather!" which is what their dad had said as they left the ranch. They all laughed and could not wait to get back and show him how crazy had worked.

The very next Sunday the brothers woke up early to a perfect day. The temperature hovered near zero, and it was forecast to remain in the single digits throughout the day with no wind.

The wind had blown furiously for the past three days, and an eerie calm greeted them when they exited the house to begin the morning chores. They all chimed together "Boys, it doesn't matter what the temperature is, if the wind ain't blowing, it's going to be a great day!" That was another one of their dad's proverbs.

After morning chores and breakfast, they changed into cold weather hunting clothes and loaded hunting gear into the '48 Chevy. Today they were heading east to a ranch which they had never hunted on before.

Their dad had met Ed, an older fellow rancher, at a bull sale, and they had started conversing about the weather, cattle, and just about everything related to ranching. When the topic of predators came up, Ed mentioned that he had an overabundance of coyotes that he needed taken care of before calving season began. Joe volunteered his boys without asking them.

When Joe approached his sons about hunting coyotes for Ed, he told them Ed's place was only 20 miles east of their place if you took the backroads. He told them that Ed was all alone and didn't have time to hunt, so it could be a gold mine for them. To seal the deal, Joe brought out a brand-new Remington Model 700 rifle chambered in the new 22-250 cartridge, with a four power Bushnell scope mounted on it. Joe said, "Here, this is for you boys. You can pay me later—just not too much later!"

The brothers couldn't believe it! They had been trying to save money to buy a rifle for Jake to replace the 22 rimfire, but it seemed like every time they were getting close, something else would come up. Joe had decided to help his boys out and knew the gun would pay for itself. Now there was no way they could say no to their dad's new friend.

They decided that John would get the new rifle, and they'd give the Remington 222 rifle to Jake. Jay said he was okay with using the sporterized Mauser but decided a scope would be nice. They agreed to go scope shopping for the Mauser rifle the next time they sold some coyote pelts.

John knew they would not be able to take any backroads to Ed's ranch as they were all blocked with snow which would turn the 20 miles into about 50 miles. But their dad had given Ed his word, and they would honor his request.

Helen made sandwiches, and she even baked apple bars and packed them with the sandwiches. When the brothers saw the bars, they realized that their mom knew what they were going through to keep Dad's word, and this was her way of saying thank you.

Jay spoke up, "I'm thinking that this trip is going to be a bust, not the gold mine dad mentioned. By the time we get there, we will probably be able to make only one calling stand. We should have headed for the refuge. You know how long we have waited for a perfect day like this to hunt it."

John answered, "Well, we are helping a new friend of our dad's today. Let's make the most of it."

Jay replied, "Well, I know the refuge, but I don't know this place."

Jake finally spoke up, "Knock it off, you two. It's a perfect day so let's get focused and get some coyotes. Ed has been a rancher his whole life, and if he says there are a lot of coyotes, I'm betting he's right." John thought that this day would probably be more of a scouting trip, but you never knew with coyotes.

When they finally entered Ed's yard, they were immediately impressed. Everything was old but well maintained. Jake said, "This for sure ain't no laying around joint."

Ed appeared from his shop, introduced himself, and invited them into the house for some coffee. The brothers declined but thanked him for the invitation and introduced themselves. "Oh," he said, "I figured out right away who was who. Joe told me all about you boys."

They asked Ed if the coyotes were howling in the evenings, and if so, where were they howling from and where was he seeing them.

Ed said, "Follow me," and he led them past a giant hip roof barn then through a feedlot where his replacement heifers were being grown out to join the herd.

The brothers stopped to admire the heifers and complemented Ed. He replied, "It has taken me a lifetime to get my herd built up to this point. You boys have good eyes for cattle."

They continued past the feedlot and his hay storage yard for 200 yards to the edge of a hill. The hill sloped gently down into a large, wooded draw which ran straight south. The draw was well over a mile long and gradually sloped up to a large complex of buttes. Right below them was another barn with several small corrals which Ed said was his calving barn for bad weather. Just beyond the barn and corrals was Ed's winter-feeding area where his herd of cows were milling around contently. Back into the trees was a small stack of baled hay inside of a fenced hay yard which could be used to feed during winter blizzards.

John had noticed that Ed put his hay up loose

in small bread loaf-like stacks which had been moved into the hay yard from his hay fields with a stack mover. When John saw this, he thought it was a smart way to put up hay when you were alone like Ed was.

There was a spring on the west side of the big draw that had been developed for watering cattle in the winter. It drained into a smaller connecting draw which sloped off to the west. It was a perfect spot to feed and shelter cattle through the winter.

They pulled out binoculars and spotted out the area while Ed said, "They howl from way back up near the buttes and travel down this draw into my feed yard every evening. I also see them in the mornings and sometimes during the day."

"Well," said John, "we're going to have to get into the draw a ways to not spook your cows."

Ed said, "They are used to shooting. I shoot at them dang coyotes every time I see them but just can't hit 'em very often. Don't worry about the cows. Heck, you boys can shoot from here if you want."

They hiked back to the '48 Chevy, and Ed left for his shop. He wished the boys good luck and insisted they stop in at the house before they left. They gathered up their calling gear and rifles and began strategizing as they hiked back to the draw.

Jay was the most excited and said, "Did you see that draw? It isn't only a perfect feed yard for cows in the winter, but it's also perfect for coyotes."

He wanted to enter the draw and set up near the stack of baled hay to call. John was not sure because the stack of baled hay could also be a perfect place for coyotes to lay up for the day, and if they walked into it, all they would accomplish was spooking coyotes back up into the wooded draw.

Jake came up with a plan that made sense. "What about the small connecting draw that the spring is flowing into? If we hike around, we won't be detected, and we can call them out of the big draw."

They all agreed it was a perfect plan. They took off hiking west, looping around into the connecting draw, and found a good spot to call from with some elevation that offered them cover and a perfect view down into a couple of open shooting lanes. When they were all in position, John turned on the cassette player that belted out a rabbit in distress sound.

They were startled when after about 30 seconds into the call, two coyotes appeared like ghosts from the main draw. John immediately turned off the cassette player, waited a few seconds, and began making a mouse-squeak sound by pulling air into his partially closed lips, causing the two coyotes to run toward them. When the two coyotes were within 50 yards, John stopped the mouse-squeak sound and began barking like a dog which brought both coyotes to a dead stop. Jay and Jake shot almost simultaneously, and both coyotes dropped in their tracks.

No one moved as they waited in silence. After five minutes had passed, John turned on the cassette player and let it play the rabbit-distress sound for 30 seconds, then he turned it off for one minute and began the sequence again. After about 15 minutes of playing the sequence, three coyotes suddenly appeared from the main draw moving cautiously into a shooting lane and stopped, using all their keen senses to identify where the distress sound was coming from.

They all knew which coyote was theirs without communicating—John left, Jay center, and Jake right. Jay whispered *one-two-three*, and they all shot at the same moment. All three coyotes dropped together as if in a ballet sequence. They couldn't believe it! Five coyotes in less than 30 minutes were laid out in front of them.

They only had two drag chains with them, so they pulled some parachute paracord out of Jay's pack and cut three pieces to serve as drag chains, then they began the long pull uphill with the five coyotes. When they reached the yard, they loaded the five coyotes into the trunk of the Chevy and packed the rest of their gear and two rifles into the backseat. Jay, who would be riding home in the front passenger seat, had the third rifle up front beside him with a full magazine but no round in the chamber, just in case they encountered any coyotes on the drive home.

They desperately wanted to take off for home, but they knew that Ed wanted to see them before they left. They went over to his shop, and it was closed, so they went over to the house and knocked on the door.

They were greeted by Ed's wife, Ethel, who insisted that they come in. When they began to pull off their boots and heavy clothing, she insisted that they didn't have to do that.

"This is a ranch house, and it's used to dirt," she said. They ignored her request and removed their boots and heavy clothing before entering anyway.

Ed was sitting at the dining room table doing some paperwork which he pushed aside and asked, "Well, how did you boys do? I heard five shots. Did you get one?"

Jake answered excitedly, "No, we got *five!*"

Ed just sat there shaking his head like their dad's unconscious habit and said, "You boys sure seem to know what you are doing, and you can for sure shoot! You're coming back, aren't you?"

Jay answered, "We sure will, if that's okay with you."

"Oh, that's okay with me" Ed replied. "You boys come back anytime, and if we aren't home, you know where to go."

Ethel brought three freshly baked giant cinnamon rolls to the table for them and asked what they wanted to drink.

"Milk, please," John, Jay, and Jake answered in unison.

John got up to help her carry the three glass-es to the table. Ed said to Ethel, "Now I know why Joe is so proud of his boys."

The table talk soon turned to cattle as the brothers peppered Ed with questions about his herd. They wanted to know everything from genetics to rations. Ed was like a dictionary full of knowledge, which he gladly shared.

Time slipped by, and John finally realized they better get going or their parents would become worried and probably come searching for them. He asked Ethel if she would call his mom and let her know that they were leaving so his parents wouldn't start worrying. "I know it will be a long-distance call," John said to Ethel as he wrote down the phone number, "but we will pay you for it."

"No, you won't!" replied Ed. "Now, you boys get going, and we will let your parents know you're on the way home ... and drive safe. It's been a pleasure meeting you, and we hope to see you soon."

Before they left, they thanked Ethel for the cinnamon rolls and Ed for allowing them to hunt. On the drive home, Jay couldn't stop talking about the big draw and what a perfect place it was for wintering cattle and calling coyotes. Jake finally asked him, "What about the refuge?"

"The *what*?" Jay answered. "That big draw is where I want to spend the rest of the winter."

"Good luck with that!" Jake said.

When they arrived back at the ranch, Jake went into the house to let Joe and Helen know they were home. Then the three brothers began unloading gear and rifles, carrying everything down to their basement bedroom where they had built a giant storage closet that held all their hunting gear. Jake stayed in the house putting the hunting gear away and cleaning rifles while John and Jay began skinning out the five coyotes and stretching them. Fleshing, sewing up bullet holes, and cleaning the fur would have to wait. They were just too tired.

John was proud of his brothers. They had worked together as a team and had shot well. It would be a day to be remembered! The new rifle had been broken in, and the five coyotes would go toward paying back their dad for it.

LETTING GO

WHO DECIDED

WHO LIVED

WHO DIED

IT WAS SO RANDOM

TO SURVIVE THE CHAOS

SOME JUST LET GO

CHAPTER 8
First Cars

John, Jay, and Jake all began driving vehicles early in their young lives. By the age of 10 they were all adept at driving the various ranch pickups and tractors. At the age of 12, John was driving the ranch pickup to small towns near the ranch that could be reached by driving on county backroads. The brothers were not allowed to drive on paved highways until they received learners' permits.

Their first car was a '48 Chevy two-door sedan that they bought together to use for hunting. John was 13, Jay 12, and Jake 11. They drove it only on back roads while hunting until they got driver permits.

John got a driver's permit when he turned 14. It required an adult with a valid driver license to accompany him while driving. The county sheriff's department ignored the rule, and kids with permits drove everywhere as if they were fully licensed during daylight hours. After dark an adult's presence was required.

John's dad helped him buy a used 1962 Chevy Nova. He would make four annual payments to his dad before the car was officially his. There were conditions that also came with the car. It was to be used only for short trips to small, nearby towns and going to and from high school during John's freshman year. Joe also warned John that if he ever caught him driving carelessly, the car would disappear instantly.

John had spotted the used Nova one morning when he was sent to town for baler parts at the local John Deere machinery dealership. The dealership also sold Chevrolet cars, pickups, and trucks. John even delayed his return to the ranch for a few minutes to look the Nova over. It was in great shape and did not have many miles on the odometer. The owner of the dealership suddenly appeared and began his standard sales pitch. John interrupted him saying, "I'm sorry, but I must get going. There's hay and my dad waiting. Just give me your best cash sale price."

That evening he spoke to his dad about the car, and they came to an agreement. The next morning Joe called the dealer and told him to put sold on the Nova. They would be in to settle up when there was a break in haying. John became more anxious every day and found himself constantly watching the sky for any sign of rain that would allow them to go to town and get the Nova.

It took a week and a half before the rain came. Joe called the dealer late in the day after it began raining. He told him to be at his dealership early the next morning and drop the price for the Nova by $100.

John could sense his mom's apprehension when they arrived home with the Nova. He told her, "Mom, you're not losing me. I am just a little more mobile now. Dad is giving me the rest of the day off, and I'm going back into town to buy insurance for my car. Let me drive you into town today for your hair appointment."

When they got to town, John took his mom to her hair appointment, then he went to the local insurance agent, Seedy Sam, to get insurance for the Nova.

The insurance agent was called Seedy Sam because he had a cousin with the same first and last name who also lived in town and was a local carpenter. To differentiate the two, the insurance agent was called Seedy Sam. He also had a seed business that sold corn, sorghum, alfalfa, and various tame and grass seed varieties. His cousin the carpenter was referred to as Carpenter Sam.

John went with the insurance program recommended by Seedy Sam, paid him, and headed back to pick up his mom. John didn't realize how long it took for a woman's hair appointment. It certainly wasn't as quick as the haircuts at the men's barber shop down the street and not as interesting either.

The local barber kept rattlesnakes he'd caught in a large glass case on a table in the corner of the barbershop. Catching and handling rattlesnakes was one of his hobbies. He also captured baby raccoons and raised them as pets and brought them to the barbershop. It was always interesting getting your haircut with a raccoon in your lap.

One day John stopped in for a haircut, and he was confronted by a young skunk sitting in the barber chair. The barber picked up the skunk and set him on the floor. John stood there at the door ready to make a quick exit until the barber told him that the skunk's scent glands had been removed by a veterinarian, and it was safe to come in. John was still skeptical especially when the skunk climbed into his lap and took a nap. It took a couple of trips back to the barbershop before he became comfortable getting his haircut with a skunk in his lap.

To pass the time, John walked down the street to the grocery store and bought a magazine to keep himself occupied while waiting for his mom. When she was finally done, he took her to a small restaurant that featured homemade apple pie and then drove her home. Helen commented on the trip home, "John, you are a very good driver, and I feel very safe driving with you."

When they got home, Helen changed into work clothes and took off for the garden. John turned his attention to the Nova. He changed the oil, greased the U-joints, drained and replaced the antifreeze, and checked the transmission and transfer case fluid levels. He then gave the Nova a good cleaning inside and out. He stood back and thought to himself, "My new car is ready to travel. I just need some more rain breaks from haying."

Jay was not allowed to purchase a car until his sophomore year in high school. John knew his parents were keeping a closer watch and tighter restrictions on Jay than they were on him. Jake and John sometimes felt sorry for Jay, but Jay was the one who was constantly testing the rules. True to form, he came home with a 1955 Chevy Bel Air two-door. The car had a white interior with a two-tone yellow and white exterior, chrome trim, which seemed to be everywhere, and a 265 turbo-fired V8 engine.

A real lady killer was what Jay called his car. Jay would spend any free time cleaning and waxing the car, performing general maintenance functions, and tuning up the engine. It was all original, and Jay intended to keep it that way. He was extremely proud of his car.

Jake was Jake, steady as a rock and a homebody. He was attached to their parents a little bit closer than either John or Jay. Jake eventually purchased a used Chevy Corvair Monza as his transportation because the price was right, and he thought it was a cool car. John and Jay thought it was a piece of junk. They were proved partially right when it was discovered that the air-cooled engine didn't quite agree with cold weather. They were constantly reminding Jake, but he didn't care. He loved that Corvair no matter what!

Having their own cars gave each one of them personnel space and freedom. John was thinking one day how he and his brothers were so alike, with the same interests, yet their cars were so different. He wondered why. Was this the beginning of them separating from each other? After some serious thought, John realized their bond was too strong for that. It didn't matter what kind of car each one of them was drawn to. Theirs was a special bond, and it was destined to last forever.

THE JUNGLE

CHANGES HAPPENED THERE

I THOUGHT I KNEW

WHO I WAS

THEN THE JUNGLE

CHANGED ME FOREVER

CHAPTER 9
High School

Being the oldest, John was the first of the brothers to enter high school in a small town located about 21 miles northwest of the ranch. At first it was a real cultural shock to go from a class of two to a class of 32.

Nancy, his only classmate for eight years in country school, was being sent to a Catholic boarding school for her high school education. John would miss her because she had become the sister he never had.

John knew quite a few of his new classmates, some from church, community picnics, Play Day competitions, and other local events, so it was not like being with a complete bunch of strangers. There were just a lot of distractions created by larger classes that he had to adjust to.

His dad allowed him to participate in fall football only if he wanted to. Basketball was out because of winter storms and the treacherous road conditions present during the winter. Spring track was also out because of calving and the associated frenzy of spring on a ranch when all available help was needed. John thought that he might try football, but he told his dad that if it interfered too much with helping on the ranch, he would drop out.

John's dad also sat him down and discussed girls, how they were to be treated, and why. He explained how girls were different from boys and like them in other ways. He also told John, "Sex will come into your life, but high school is not the place for it."

John had kind of figured all of this out already, but he still gave his dad his undivided attention. He could sense that this was not easy for his dad to talk about and appreciated him taking the time and effort to discuss such matters with him personally.

To get to the high school, John would drive to the little local community located on a state highway west of the ranch and then ride a school bus north to a larger town where the high school was located. During fall football season, he could drive all the way to attend high school and football practice after school.

John liked football and became a substitute for various positions on defense and offense his very first year of playing. You could instantly tell which players milked cows by hand because they never dropped a football.

After the first season, John became a starting linebacker on defense and a starting tight end on offense. John liked the physical contact and the intrinsic nature of the game and teamwork required for success. When John was on the field, the crowd and all background noise disappeared. His total focus was the other 21 players on the field. They were all that he saw and heard. This total concentration allowed him to react instantly to an opposing team's plays giving him a distinct advantage. This level of concentration was a skill that he had learned while hunting. To John it seemed normal, and he assumed everyone had it.

Games against rival high school teams in the area were held on Friday evenings. A school bus was used to transport the team to and from games, and John was required to leave for home immediately after being returned to the high school grounds. John knew better than to fool around. His parents knew too many people, and he didn't want to mess up football by disobeying his parents' rules, but it still was hard to leave for home and not stay to celebrate a win with his teammates.

John went to a basketball game once and left at halftime. He never did attend another one. The noise and commotion were overwhelming, and the game just did not interest him. Heck, if you bumped a guy, it immediately became a penalty. John could not get excited about a game that did not allow physical contact.

John found certain high school subjects chal-lenging, especially algebra and chemistry. He would sit on the bus with Sally, a neighbor girl in his class, every morning and evening. She offered to help him with homework.

Sally had gone to another country school six miles south of the one John and his brothers at-tended, and he knew her through Play Day events. She was extremely intelligent and helped John immensely with challenging subjects. She went on to become a medical doctor. Sally would not give John answers, only clues, and he would have to figure out the problem from there. Her clues were calculated and precise which helped John every time.

John and Sally dated occasionally. John thought it was the least he could do to repay her, plus she was not so serious and sometimes even helped John pull pranks on friends.

Sally's favorite prank was one they thought up together at the drive-in movie theater one eve-ning. The back row was known as lovebird row. It was where couples parked that made out instead of watching the movie. There was a shelterbelt full of trees directly behind the back row, and Sally and John decided that would be a perfect place to sneak up to a parked car and then escape later.

The next week Sally and John went to the drive-in prepared for the prank. They selected their victims, then they put on hooded sweatshirts and wrapped bandannas around their faces. They snuck through the shelterbelt and found the couple they had selected who were busy making out in the front seat. They doused them with squirt guns through both open front windows, then made a successful escape.

Sally enjoyed the prank immensely and helped John pull the same prank now and then— that was until she and another classmate she started dating became the victims! She wouldn't help John with homework for two weeks after that.

When the country roads became blocked with snow during snowstorms, John and other classmates stayed overnight in an old post office in the small community west of the ranch and then rode the bus to high school the next morning. There was a widow who lived in a small house attached to the back of what used to be the community post office. For a fee she would feed and provide cots within the old post office for children unable to make it home during storms. It was a barracks-like facility without much privacy except for the bathroom. Girls slept on one end of the old post office and boys on the other end. There was a curtain attached to the ceiling which separated the two living areas, and once the lights were out, you'd better not get caught on the wrong side of it or even go near it to sneak a peek.

The widow even had a TV and various games to keep the snowbound children occupied. The students were also allowed to use her phone to call their parents. Jake would call home repeatedly, and he was finally cut back to one call per evening. Everyone followed the rules because if they didn't, their parents would be informed.

John, and eventually his brothers Jay and Jake, were forced to stay there a couple of times a year. John never thoroughly enjoyed the stay as he missed his own personal space and privacy that home allowed, and it was impossible to get any homework done there. Jay always had a blast, especially if there were girls his age also staying overnight.

Jay and Jake also both played football and were good at it. Jay became the team's primary running back on offense, and like John, a linebacker on defense. He was fearless and the fastest player the coach had ever witnessed. Jake became the team's fullback on offense and a linebacker on defense. He was a textbook blocker and tackler and the coach's favorite player.

For two years, all three played together as starters on defense and offense, and the O'Janon brothers became a force to be reckoned with. Competing team coaches were extremely glad when the O'Janon boys finally graduated from high school.

Helen initially accompanied Joe to home football games to watch their sons play but she had to stop. She was startled at the extreme level of violence exhibited by her sons toward opposing team members and feared for their safety. Her sons were not the same boys she interacted with every day. How could they change so drastically?

She didn't want to see them like that but was proud that at the end of the game when both teams lined up and shook hands. Her sons all exhibited respect and did not taunt the other team's members even after they had beaten them badly. *Maybe that's my half,* she thought.

John occasionally dated and found communicating with girls enlightening. Their views on life and current events were slightly different, and they stimulated him to contemplate his own views. He did not have a steady girlfriend like many of his classmates. He just hadn't met the right girl, and it seemed if he was interested in one, she was already going steady. John also was not ready for commitment in his life, and he enjoyed the freedom of not having a steady girlfriend. He liked their company, and he also enjoyed the making out part of dating, but he always heeded his dad's advice about girls in the back of his mind.

Jay had a steady girlfriend his freshman year and successive ones all the way through high school. Girls just came at him from all directions, and Jay thoroughly enjoyed their company in more ways than one.

Jay and a friend of his named Hank went into the local drugstore one day. According to Hank, Jay walked directly to the pharmacist behind the counter and asked for condoms. The pharmacist looked at Jay and said, "You're a little young for those, aren't you?"

Jay looked him in the eye and said, "And I'm also a little young to be a dad."

The pharmacist looked back at Jay, shaking his head, and asked, "How many do you want?"

Hank could not believe what he had just witnessed. But when Hank tried the same line at the pharmacy the next day, he was told to get lost.

Jake pretty much followed John's path and had occasional dates but nothing serious until the beginning of his senior year when he fell in love, or *puppy love* as John and Jay called it. Jake hated the phrase and would ignore them when they ribbed him about his new girlfriend. His steady girlfriend was Sally's younger sister, Shirley. They were inseparable until they both graduated, and he joined the Army while she went off to college. They still communicated regularly by mail or phone and had plans for a life together after Jake got out of the Army.

The brothers also had fun with pranks being covertly pulled on fellow classmates. The best one was with a classmate of Jay's named Mickey who wished to match Jay's prowess with the opposite sex. He was always attaching himself to Jay hoping to attract girls to himself.

Mickey just wasn't a Jay or even a John or Jake. He had no athletic abilities and was extremely clumsy. His one attribute was scholarly abilities. He received the best grades in every class he attended.

One day he ran Jay down in the hallway between classes. Mickey was beaming and so excited that he could barely speak. "She said yes! She said yes!" was all that Jay could understand at first.

Apparently, Mickey had asked an ex-girlfriend of Jay's to a school dance, and she had accepted. Mickey had their entire date planned out detail by detail and was going to borrow his mother's VW Beetle. Mickey was going to drive out to Sharon's parent's farm and pick her up and take her into town to the school's gymnasium where a Friday night school dance was being held. After the dance, on the way back to her parent's farm, he would pull over to visit and that would hopefully result in a making-out session.

Mickey was on cloud nine the entire week and extremely anxious for Friday night to arrive. None of the brothers were attending the dance, but they made a covert trip to town Friday night with bricks in the trunk of Jay's car. Locating Mickey's mom's VW Beetle in the school's parking lot was not too difficult since it was the only one in town.

John and Jay lifted the back end of the Beetle while Jake placed bricks under each axle on both sides just inside the rear wheels. Then they set the Beetle back down onto the bricks which kept both back wheels suspended, just barely off the ground. They repeated the process with the front of the Beetle. Jay and John tried to rock the beetle, but it held solid. They sat on it while Jake checked to make sure that all four wheels didn't make any contact with the ground.

When they were convinced that everything was perfect, they went home remembering their dad's advice, "Don't get caught," and then they became as anxious as Mickey had been before his date.

Monday seemed to never arrive. Mickey told the story to Jay at lunch time. Everything was going perfectly. Sharon seemed to be enjoying the dance and his company, and when they left the dance and got into his mom's VW Beetle, Mickey could sense a making-out session with Sharon was in his future.

The Beetle started with no problem, but when he put it in gear and let out the clutch, it wouldn't move. He tried every gear plus reverse, but the Beetle just wouldn't move. Mickey got out and checked the front and back wheels for obstructions, but he couldn't see anything. All that he could think was he had ruined the transmission, and his mom wouldn't be happy.

Mickey was able to find a ride home for Sharon with some friends who lived near her parents' farm and was sure that she would never date him again. He walked down the street to his house, and the next morning, he was awakened early by his mom wanting to know where her car was. She was not pleased when he explained what had happened after the dance in the school parking lot.

It was Saturday and Mickey and his mom

waited impatiently for Mickey's dad to awaken. He always slept in on Saturdays. When his dad finally got up, all three of them walked to the school parking lot which was empty except for the Beetle. Mickey's dad started it and was trying all the gears when Mickey's mom noticed that the wheels were spinning but the car wasn't moving.

His dad got out and crawled as far under the Beetle as he could and started laughing so hard, he began to cough. Mickey with his mom started to pull him out when he said, "No, you've both got to see this!"

Mickey pleaded with Jay, "You've got to help me find out who did this so I can get even."

Jay agreed to help him discover whoever was responsible and help Mickey get even when they found out who it was. He also told him to not give up on Sharon. It sounded like she really liked him, and he should ask her for another date.

Sharon agreed to another date, just not in the Beetle. Jay loaned Mickey his 1955 Chevy for the date, and Sharon and Mickey continued dating throughout high school. They never could discover who was responsible for the prank. Mickey always kept an ear to the ground waiting for a clue, hoping to discover the guilty party.

It wasn't until the high school graduation party that Jay finally told the truth about the prank. Then Jay let Sharon and Mickey hold him down and pour beer all over him.

High school seemed to fly by for John, and he

missed it when it was over, but he was glad to get through it. He eagerly looked forward to getting on with his life.

The brothers were all offered football athletic scholarships upon graduating from high school from just about every college in their state. They had a serious discussion one evening about Vietnam, and all three of them decided that they were going to enlist in the Army after high school before going on with their education in college.

The choice was theirs, but not going when your country called seemed dishonorable to them. They had been raised with the belief that freedom had to be earned, not just inherited. Deep down they naively wanted to experience what their dad had experienced.

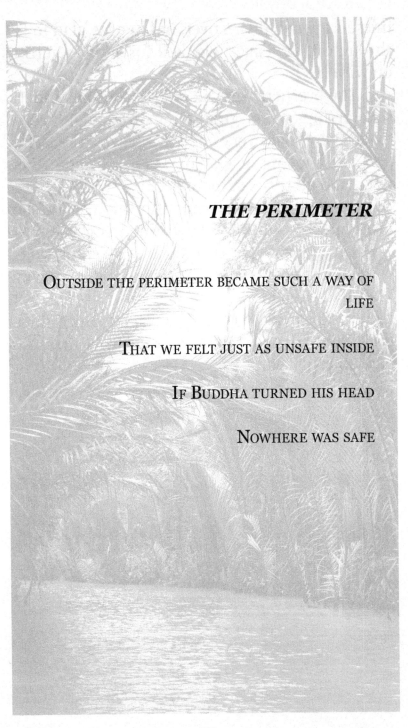

THE PERIMETER

OUTSIDE THE PERIMETER BECAME SUCH A WAY OF
LIFE

THAT WE FELT JUST AS UNSAFE INSIDE

IF BUDDHA TURNED HIS HEAD

NOWHERE WAS SAFE

CHAPTER 10
Basic Training

John was only 17 when he graduated from high school. It would be another six months before he turned 18. His parents had to sign a letter of consent when he signed up for the Army through a recruiter who came to his high school during the middle of his senior year.

John had planned on staying home for the summer to help on the ranch. His dad told him they would be fine without him for the summer, and he should go as soon as possible to get military service over with and be able to move on with his life.

He also gave John some advice about basic training—never volunteer for anything, never ever stare at the drill sergeant, and do everything you are told to do promptly. Then he put his hands on John's shoulders, looked him in the eye, and said, "Now remember, this is a serious business you are getting yourself into. Find people who you can trust and keep them close."

John left for his medical checkup and indoctrination process 300 miles to the east of the ranch just after noon on a blustery spring day a week after he had graduated from high school. This was John's very first bus trip, and he assumed it would be a leisurely trip until he realized that the bus stopped in every small town along the route and a couple of larger ones. The bus stopped even if there were no passengers or packages to pick up or drop off.

To John it seemed as if the trip took forever. Then he remembered his dad telling him that there would be a lot of waiting around in the Army. John leaned back in his seat, closed his eyes, and thought, *Why is my dad always so right?*

Later the next day, after physicals and indoctrination, the entire group of new recruits was put on a train which left immediately for an Army base on the West Coast where they would begin their basic training. The barracks of the base were extremely old and looked exactly as his dad had described them. John looked around and wondered if he was in the same building his dad had been in. Then he remembered his dad's words, "Enjoy them while you're there. If I remember right, the accommodations keep going downhill."

All John could do was look around and wonder what he'd gotten himself into. He found the physical demands of basic training much easier than the recruiter had described, and he especially enjoyed and excelled in weapons training. Because he was able to perform above the required physical standards, completed all assigned tasks promptly and correctly, and stayed out of trouble, John was not subjected to the constant badgering and harassment administered to some recruits by the drill sergeant and training NCOs (noncommissioned officers). They had their hands full with recruits that were unable to meet minimum physical requirements, had an unfamiliarity with weapons, and demonstrated an inability to complete assigned tasks promptly and correctly. John helped his fellow recruits whenever he could, and it seemed at times like he was spending as much time helping train his teammates as a training NCO.

John met the first person he felt he could truly trust on the very first day of basic training even before their heads had been shaved and any facial hair removed. Military uniforms and related gear had also not been issued yet, and they were still wearing the clothes in which they had arrived.

John had never met a hippie and didn't know exactly what to expect when a fellow recruit with long unkempt hair and an equally long unkempt beard dressed in what looked like hand-me-down clothing approached John and introduced himself. Nick was from California, and he'd lived out of a tent that he would put up in various parks and open areas within the towns he encountered while hitchhiking up and down the coast. He crafted things from discarded objects he'd found in city dumps and sold them to tourists and residents as art. His specialty was wire coat hangers he would bend into *pieces of art* as he called them.He had been pursuing this lifestyle for over two years and evidently made enough income to survive.

Nick said, "Everything was going great, really groovy. Then I got super high one night, and the next thing I remembered was being on a military bus a few days later, and now, here I am."

John had to ask what *super high* meant, and Nick burst out laughing. Then he asked, "Where are you from?"

When John told him where he was from and about the ranch, Nick couldn't stop asking questions. It almost made John feel like a foreigner from another country, but Nick wanted to know every detail of life on a ranch. Sometimes when they were talking about the ranch, it seemed as if Nick was trying to transpose himself onto the ranch. He just could not get enough and was always pressing John for more information.

Nick had proclaimed himself as a conscientious objector who would do his duty and serve his country as required, but he would not harm another person no matter what the circumstances were. He was scheduled to attend medic training immediately after graduating from basic training.

John had to step in now and then to straighten out fellow recruits who tried to harass Nick because he was a conscientious objector. John knew about medics from his dad. "The bravest man in your platoon will be the medic," his dad had told him one day. "Treat him with respect and protect him at all costs."

Nick became a good soldier. John knew he would become a great medic, a man you would want at your side.

John's dad had instructed him to never look at the drill sergeant, but the man mesmerized him so much that he started staring at him. This caught the drill sergeant's attention. He immediately rushed over and got in front of John screaming, "What are you looking at me for, private!"

John answered, "I was admiring you and hoping to learn how to become a good soldier by watching you."

They both stood looking into each other eyes without blinking. Finally, the drill sergeant took a step back and said, "Private, you are now squad leader of third squad. Now, move back to your squad! Apply yourself and follow orders or this is going to get real personal between you and me, understand? Then he screamed, "Third squad! Send someone up to this position, *now!*"

John responded, "Yes, Drill Sergeant, I will do my best," while thinking to himself, *Now I know why my dad gave me the drill sergeant advice.* Then he thought to himself, *I just got volunteered and I certainly cannot write home to dad and explain to him how I became a squad leader.*

John had never done so many push-ups in his life. Push-ups were the primary punishment that the recruits endured for any real or imagined infraction while in training. Recruits were required to drop in place immediately even if they were standing in a couple inches of water or ankle deep in mud and perform the requested number of push-ups without stopping for a break. If they stopped or touched the ground with anything besides the palms of their hands and toes, they were required to start over with the drill sergeant or one of his assistants standing over them screaming a barrage of derogatory remarks nonstop. If a recruit was carrying his rifle, he had to be extra cautious and not allow it to touch the ground. This was accomplished by placing it on the back of both hands while performing the required number of push-ups.

One of the trainees in fourth squad named Howard seemed to struggle with just about everything. He especially had problems doing push-ups. One day Howard was having issues and could not complete a training exercise. This infuriated the training NCO who made Howard drop and do push-ups. Howard could not do all the requested push-ups or keep his rifle off the ground, and this infuriated the training NCO even more. After the platoon was marched back to the base, Howard spent the entire evening and a good part of the night at the armory cleaning every rifle in the platoon. After he cleaned each rifle, he was then required to do five push-ups with the rifle balanced on the back of his hands before he could begin cleaning the next one.

His squad had to practically dress him the next morning to make the morning formation on time. They helped carry his gear on the march out to a remote training site and then took turns keeping him awake for the training class. John felt sorry for Howard. He was a nice guy who always tried. He just lacked physical abilities. By the end of basic training, Howard was no Charles Atlas, but through extra effort on his part, he was able to finish just about every exercise. He was usually last but always proud to have finished.

The second person John encountered that he knew could be trusted was a fellow squad member named Converse. Converse was a Sioux Indian who had grown up on a remote Indian reservation. Converse's goal was to return to the reservation from the war in Vietnam with a chest full of medals. He cared about his fellow soldiers, and he was constantly helping someone complete a task or finish an obstacle. John and Converse had both grown up hunting and trapping and would spend spare time discussing techniques and successes or failures they had experienced while hunting and trapping.

Converse also told John a lot about growing up on a reservation, and it did not sound like a great place to have been raised, but Converse had persevered and took pride in his warrior heritage and in being a soldier. Converse never could understand all the complaining by the other trainees about the mess hall food. One day, he told John that he had never eaten so good in his life, and he always enjoyed and consumed everything that was served.

Despite their youth, they both recognized the enormity of what they were about to encounter and trained hard together to prepare themselves. John liked Converse from the moment they met, and he could see that he was a man you would want at your side in battle.

A lot of the trainees did not like the policy of an entire squad being punished because one of their members could not perform training exercises properly. Second squad had a guy named Ray who was about five years older than the rest of the squad members. He had a negative, self-centered attitude and balked at taking orders from the squad leader who was younger than him. He also did not apply himself to training. He thought it was a waste of his time and would not coordinate effectively with the rest of the squad in squad-related training exercises.

This resulted in the squad failing the exercise and being punished. The squad had become a dysfunctional unit because of one member. When Ray began to blame the rest of the squad for the constant punishment, the squad leader confronted Ray. Ray began shouting and then pushing the squad leader around which led to the whole squad becoming involved. The encounter ended up with Ray getting a beating from the squad.

The drill sergeant and his training assistants noticed the bruises on Ray the next morning but did not investigate. It was like they knew Ray was the reason for the squad's poor performance, and this was what they had been waiting for—the squad to come together and straighten Ray out.

Two days later Ray approached John and asked if he could get him transferred to his squad because they seemed to get along so well. John sat quietly for a while looking at Ray and then answered, "That's not how things work in the Army. We go where we're told and do what we're told to do. Your squad gets along fine except for you. You have a negative attitude and you're not applying yourself to training. This is war we're training for. The training may seem dumb to us right now, but I'm betting we'll be glad for all of it someday. Teamwork and commitment to our squad is what I see as the main thing that they are trying to teach us. Now, you go back to your squad, apply yourself and follow orders, or you can stay on the course you are on. But remember, once we get to Vietnam, the only way you are going to survive is by counting on the man next to you!"

A few weeks later, Ray's squad leader came up to John and asked, "What did you say to Ray? He has completely changed. The squad is finally starting to work together like a team."

John answered, "I just told him to focus on

what's ahead of us, war!"

The rifle range was John's favorite part of training. One day the range officer came up to John and asked, "Private, where did you learn to shoot like that?"

Without thinking John answered, "Rast-ich so Rost-ich."

"Do not get smart with me, Private!" the range officer screamed.

John said, "Sorry, Lieutenant, it means *When I rest, I rust*. An older friend of mine scribed it into the stock of my first gun and explained that it was not just meant for the gun but also me. If you want to shoot good, you must shoot."

The range officer smiled and said, "Your friend sounds like an incredibly wise man."

After that the two became friends. One day the range officer asked John to shoot his personal rifle which had been rebuilt and accurized by the battalion's chief armor. After John shot the rifle at a distant target, they walked out to view the target and the range officer said, "Shit, I always suspected that the gun was better than me. Now get out of here, Private, before I assign you some push-ups!"

The pugil pit was where John met Big Jim and fought him to a tie. After they had beaten the heck out of each other with pugil sticks, they developed a respect for each other that evolved into a friendship.

The pugil pit was a shallow hole dug into the ground with bleachers around it. Two soldiers put on old football helmets and were given pugil sticks. Pugil sticks were round, straight, wooden sticks with padded ends the approximate length of a rifle. They were used to train soldiers how to use a rifle in hand-to-hand combat. Two soldiers jumped into the pit and began swinging until one went down and became the loser. The competition would continue with only winners advancing until there were just two soldiers left for one final match to determine the platoon winner.

Big Jim and John both advanced and ended up being the last two winners. They wound up fighting each other in the final match. Big Jim was six feet six and built like a bodybuilder. Everything was muscle combined with strength and speed. He claimed to have never been beaten in a street fight or physical challenge. Big Jim could not believe it when the drill sergeant finally stopped their match and declared a tie. John congratulated Big Jim. Apparently, no opponent had ever done anything like that, and Big Jim walked away without responding.

After that John began approaching Big Jim during breaks, and he started communicating. John found out Big Jim had suffered a very traumatic upbringing and had spent most of his childhood being bounced from one foster care home to another. When he learned about John's growing up on a ranch and ranching, he decided that it sounded like a better life than he had been living. He decided when he got out of the service, he would pursue a life on a ranch, fighting with cows instead of people.

"No," John said," "it's best not to try and fight with a cow because you'll lose. Cows are not too bright, but they are very predictable, and if you take your time and handle them right, you can usually get a cow to do what you want. Save the fighting for when you have the right tools in hand like ropes, horses, corrals, and head gates. It will be much safer for you and the cow."

Big Jim began modeling himself after John, and he started helping other recruits complete obstacles and tasks. One day he told John that he'd never felt so good about himself in his entire life.

One day while on break Converse asked John, "Why is the drill sergeant such a hard ass that never lets up?"

John thought about it for a moment and answered, "Because it's his role to play our enemy. Just think about it. Everyone hates him. The key word is *everyone*, which means he has accomplished his main goal—bonding us together and getting us to focus on our current enemy."

"Damn you, John," Converse said. "Sometimes I don't know why I ask you anything and then I know."

FLASHBACKS

Can't remember except in a flash

Going back only for moments

Bits and pieces of the past

Come and go from nowhere

Or was it really somewhere

Faces without names

Places without reality

Everything's like a dream

That makes me want to scream

CHAPTER 11
Advanced Individualized Training

Upon completion of basic training, John and a portion of the company he was in were marched across the base for Advanced Individualized Training (AIT). Their Military Occupational Specialty (MOS) was Eleven Bravo which meant that they were being trained to become infantrymen.

The march felt like a giant catwalk, with the troops being bombarded with slang every time they encountered another unit. They were called dead ducks, fresh meat, ground pounders, suckers, and other military jargon they tried to ignore, but the tirade never let up until they arrived at their new company area.

Compared to basic training, AIT was almost liberating. The physical requirements weren't as strenuous, and the constant badgering and harassment were almost absent. John was impressed with the massive firepower afforded to an infantry company and beginning to feel a little more secure about his situation until he began learning about the enemy they would be facing and their tactics.

Besides the weapons and tactical training John was receiving, he strived to learn all he could about Mr. Charlie, which is what their instructors called the North Vietnamese and Viet Cong soldiers.

One of his training NCOs, Sergeant Necco, who had served two tours in Vietnam, became intrigued with John's desire for knowledge about the Viet Cong and North Vietnamese soldiers he would soon be facing in battle, and he began to share everything he knew about the enemy with John.

Sergeant Necco was constantly reminding John that booby traps were an infantry man's worst enemy. To help John learn how to detect them, he would take John back into the woods and have him patrol trails where he had set up nonlethal booby traps. John thought he would be good at detecting trip wires, Bouncing Betties, and hand-detonated mines, but after traversing a few trails, he knew he had a lot of learning to do.

With Sergeant Necco's help, John eventually became extremely proficient at detecting booby traps. One leaf on a trail pointing in a different direction from the rest of the leaves, a slight depression or irregularity in the trail, plant disturbance off to the side of a trail, all became warning signs for John.

One evening during a break while they were both on company watch, Sergeant Necco asked, "John, why do you want to know so much about Mr. Charlie?"

John thought about it for a moment and answered, "I guess I can't help it because it's how we learned to hunt back on the ranch. If you didn't know your prey, they would come out on top every time. Then John said, "Can I ask you a question?"

Sergeant Necco nodded, and John continued. "With all the firepower available to the Army, why is this war still going on? Then, if you add in the Marines, Navy, and Air Force, plus the South Vietnamese forces, who could stand up to that?"

Sergeant Necco looked long and hard at John and replied, "Son, you need to be able to see through the smoke. This war is being grossly mismanaged, and it's probably not going to change, so when you get over there, be extremely cautious, take care of the man next to you, and survive. That'll be your win because we're never going to win this war."

John was glad to be training with a lot of the same people from basic training especially Converse and Big Jim. He also met some new people in AIT training that he hoped he would be serving with in Vietnam.

Leon was a tall, lean black guy from Seattle. John had been able to see portions of that city when the train they'd ridden from the indoctrination center back home entered Seattle to deposit them at a huge train station within the city limits. A military bus waited to take them to the base where they began their military careers.

John had never seen anything so huge. The city seemed to go on forever, and the buildings were taller than any he had ever seen in his life. John could not imagine what it would have been like growing up in such a huge place and with so many people around you.

John noticed Leon struggling one day and went over to assist him. Leon said, "I thought you white crackers only helped one another."

While helping Leon, John answered, "Once we get to the war, I'll be depending on you just as much as you'll be depending on me, so we might as well start now."

That began their friendship and Leon and John both became fascinated with each other's experiences growing up, one from a huge city and one from the *middle of nowhere*, as Leon called the ranch. Leon taught John a lot about what it was like growing up in a huge city. One day he told John that at first, he'd thought John was a real hick from nowhere, but after learning about John's life growing up on a ranch, it sounded much better than his life had been growing up in Seattle.

John told Leon, "Are you crazy? Look at your summers. You and your friends had so many things to do and lots of interesting places to go to. It was like your summer breaks from school were a vacation, and when you were older and got jobs, you had set hours and a guaranteed wage. Sounds to me like you had it rather good. Look at me and my brothers. All we did was work everyday sunup to sundown except for a Sunday afternoon off now and then."

Leon stared off looking down the barracks and said, "No, you don't understand. Most of the people that I grew up with would have become much better people if they had been brought up like you and your brothers were."

Near the end of their AIT training the entire company was required to go on one last bivouac. Word was that it was going to be a grueling three-day foray into the most remote area on the base. They would be marching in combat formation and camping overnight for two nights. They were instructed to pack their heavy winter wool gear because the forecast was calling for some snow while they were out and to pack enough C-Rations for three days. When they were all geared up with the heavy wool clothing and carrying their rifles, John estimated each one of them would be packing somewhere over 90 pounds.

They left early on a frosty morning hours before the sun would show itself. Despite the low early morning temperature, John had instructed his squad to dress light for the march. They were not incredibly happy at first, but as the day lengthened, they were glad for John's advice. Just about everyone else in the company had dressed too warmly and began sweating profusely in the heavy

ADVANCED INDIVIDUALIZED TRAINING

wool gear. Later in the day when the temperature began to drop, most of them began shivering uncontrollably.

During a short break later during the evening march, John had his squad put on some of their heavy wool gear. Looking over at the squad next to them, John said, "Those poor bastards are going to freeze tonight!"

They had been informed that both bivouacs would be combat style, meaning no campfires or small Sterno cans of heat that could be purchased at the PX would be allowed. Each platoon would also be required to post two-man perimeter security guards in two-hour watch cycles during the night.

Toward evening, after a long grueling march, the first night's bivouac site was finally reached. Each of the four platoons was assigned to a designated area and then each squad in the platoon was assigned to their spot. They all began by pairing up and erecting the two-man pup tents and arranging the rest of the gear inside and near the tent, ready for inspection before they could eat. They were told there would be no smoking after dark.

John had paired up with Leon, and they quickly erected the pup tent and placed all their gear properly in place for inspection so they could eat. As they sat there eating cold rations, John looked around and was impressed at how neat and orderly the entire company area looked with tents placed about in an orderly fashion.

John had to attend a platoon briefing for guard duty assignments and come up with a schedule for the night security detail. The night passed uneventfully except for the weather. The temperature had dropped considerably, and it seemed destined to stay on the colder side.

The next morning, they ate a cold canned breakfast of C-Rations, then dismantled the tents, rolled up sleeping bags, and packed up for the to-day's march. They policed up their assigned camp-ing areas, formed up, and began marching through a dense forest toward the next night's bivouac site.

About noon, huge, dark, ominous clouds rolled in. It began snowing lightly at first, and then increased in intensity. A strong, northwest wind suddenly developed, and along with the snow, be-gan to cause visibility problems. The company trudged on into the abyss as conditions seemed to worsen by the minute, and it was becoming diffi-cult keeping track of one another. Within an hour they were in the center of a full-blown blizzard. In places the snow was waist deep, and visibility was close to zero.

The march was halted in a small meadow, and the troops were instructed to begin erecting tents. The company was going to shelter in place. It was not an orderly event like the previous night as troops began shoveling snow with E-tools (en-trenching tools) to clear areas for the tents. They soon became disoriented with squad members becoming disconnected from their squads.

As they were shoveling side by side, Leon asked John, "Did you see that giant rock we passed back along the trail?"

John answered, "Yes, but barely."

"Well," Leon said, "I got a good look at it, and it would be a perfect place to set up a tent and ride out this storm."

"Do you want to go?" John answered, "Do you think we can find it?"

Leon said, "You were born and raised in this shit. You will find it. Now let's get out of here! Most of these tents will be buried by morning."

It wasn't difficult to disconnect from the company in the mayhem. No one noticed them leave, and even though it had been obliterated in places, John was able to follow the trail made by the company. They almost passed by the giant rock, but Leon noticed it. They left the trail and struggled through the snow to the rock. What they discovered was amazing! At the base of the rock was a small, open, cave-like overhang completely sheltered from the wind and snow.

There was room to erect the pup tent, and Leon ventured out and came back with a load of broken branches. They dug a fire pit and built a small fire which heated up the area, making it amazingly comfortable. Leon had filled the bottom of his ruck pack with cans of Sterno that were lit and placed around the shelter for additional heat.

"See, I ain't no dummy!" Leon boasted as he pulled the cans from his pack.

"Yeah, but if you had been caught with even one can, you would've been placed on permanent KP duty," John said.

"But I'm not getting caught, am I?" Leon said, as he pulled out a box of grape nut cereal.

Leon always carried a box of grape nut cereal with him and snacked on it while marching. They munched on it between sips of water. When their water got low, they would fill their mess cups with snow and melt it over the fire.

"Now this is how to camp in a blizzard," Leon boasted. "Glad you could join me, John."

They stayed up late into the night conversing about life before the Army and plans after the Army. Then they crawled into the pup tent, zipped up into their sleeping bags, and slept soundly through the rest of the night with the blizzard raging wildly literally feet from them.

The next morning, they both awoke at the same time in a panic mode. They had slept in, which was not part of the plan. They tore down the pup tent, packed up all their gear, and policed up the area in record time before they even noticed the dead calm surrounding them.

The storm had subsided as fast as it had appeared. They departed quickly, hoping to slip in as covertly as they had left.

The amount of snow left by the storm was astronomical. They took turns breaking a trail back toward the bivouac site. John had taken a compass reading last night on the hike to the rock and had to redirect Leon at times. "Dam this white shit is becoming a pain in the ass," Leon said after a stint of breaking trail. No offense meant."

"None taken," answered John, "but I was thinking, you would be a lot easier to find in all this white shit than me."

"Well," Leon answered, "I never thought of it that way and only you would."

They both started laughing. John was pushing forward at such a frantic pace that Leon finally stopped him, and asked, "John, why are you in such a hurry? We will make it back but not if we kill ourselves doing it."

John said, "I am concerned about the rest of the squad. You know as squad leader I feel bad that I left them last night."

"John, you lifer," Leon answered. "They will be fine. You have done such a good job teaching them how to think for themselves that I know they figured something out."

After about an hour of pushing and digging their way through the snow, they could hear but not see the company. They stopped for a break, relieved that this part of last night's ordeal was nearly over. Leon's expression became serious as he said, "John, I doubt we will be able to return without being noticed. This must remain our secret. I do not want you to get in trouble because I didn't want to spend the night buried under this damn snow in a tent. Let me do the talking. Do you understand?"

John did not know what Leon had planned but he had what John viewed as street smarts and trusted him, so he responded, "Yes, I understand! It will remain our secret. You have my word. Now go save our asses. I have got to find the rest of our squad and make sure they're okay."

When they came within sight of the company, they were immediately noticed, and a soldier from first squad came rushing up saying, "Follow me. I've got to get you to the command area. They're organizing search teams for you right now."

"But my squad," John protested, "I've got to make sure they're okay."

"Your platoon lieutenant is at the command area. He will know about your squad. Now, follow me."

Just as John had suspected, when they entered the command post, everyone rushed forward with a million questions all at once. John found the company commander and requested permission to leave and find his squad to make sure they were okay. John also did not want to be around for the intense questioning which would be forthcoming about his and Leon's supposed struggles for survival.

The company commander noted John's concern and turned to John's platoon lieutenant who said, "John, your squad is fine. They came through the night in better shape than any other squad in the company."

Leon stepped in and began explaining in precise detail how they became disoriented and lost in the blizzard and had spent the entire night moving nonstop through the blinding snow thinking that it was their best chance for survival. The captain finally stopped Leon and ordered the private from first squad to take them to the aid station where troops were being treated for hypothermia and frostbite while awaiting transport back to the base by medivac helicopters.

The entire area was a mess with troops shoveling snow everywhere digging out pup tents and gear. There was even a squad shoveling out a landing area for the helicopters.

"Damn," the private said as he was leading them to the aid station, "I was looking forward to getting away from this mess searching for you two. The captain has ordered that every piece of gear be accounted for before we head back to the base, even tent stakes. We will be sifting through this snow for days. Can you believe it?"

The medics thoroughly examined John and Leon, and they were surprised at their stable conditions but insisted on hooking them up to IV tubes and tagging them for extraction. On the helicopter flight out, Leon looked over at John and said, "This is how to travel through this damn white snow! Glad you could join me, John."

They were examined again back at the base hospital and forced to stay overnight and then re-

leased. They had the whole barracks to themselves, and with literally no one around, they
lounged around waiting for the company to return. That evening after finishing a game of check-
ers, Leon leaned back and said, "Now this is how
to serve in the Army. Glad you could join me,
John."

John was anxious for the company to return,
but he again felt bad because they would be forced
to march back. He especially wanted to hear his
squad's story about the ordeal from men like Joe,
the Eskimo from Alaska, and Billy, a hillbilly from
South Carolina. They both knew how to spin a
yarn.

But it was Sam, a Mexican from New Mexico,
that John was the most anxious to hear from. Sam
had become John's right-hand man in the squad,
and if it were not for his extremely quiet manner
and shyness, would have made a perfect squad
leader. Sam was so extremely observant that nothing ever needed to be explained twice. His memory recall abilities never stopped amazing John.

When the company got back to the base, they
looked like they had been through hell or something like it. They were all given one day of rest
before training would resume with a vengeance
because they had now fallen behind schedule.

Sam, Joe, Billy, and the rest of the squad gathered around John and Leon, and they exchanged
their experiences from the Night from Hell, which
was what the company's troops were calling the

bivouac outing. John still had mixed feelings about not sharing the truth with the squad. He knew if the truth were told, it would eventually spread to command. John was willing to take any punishment, but he did not want to see Leon get in trouble, so he allowed Leon to tell the cover-up story. It was their secret, never to be shared.

John was impressed with how Sam had stepped up and taken charge of the squad. Sam had found a *sweet spot* as he called it, where there was reasonable cover from the wind and snow. It was an area only large enough for two pup tents, so that's what they erected, and then they squeezed four men with sleeping bags into each tent. There was no sleeping, but with the sleeping bags and their body heat, they remained safe from hypothermia and frostbite throughout the night.

They had realized early on that John and Leon were missing, but Sam had made the right decision to not venture out looking for them. They were all worried, but they knew if two men could survive the night, it would be John and Leon.

John sat there remembering his dad's words as he departed for training and thought, *Well, Dad. I've found people I trust, and they would even make you proud.*

When John graduated from Advanced Individualized Training, he was scheduled to fly across country to Fort Benning, Georgia, for three weeks of Airborne Training, but he was informed at the last minute that he had been bumped back to the next class. John was given a choice to skip jump school or wait three weeks and attend the next class. He decided to wait it out, but he wasn't looking forward to being the company errand boy for three weeks. He had always wanted to feel the exhilaration of jumping out of an airplane and viewing the earth while floating down in a parachute. There were also a few extra dollars a month he would receive called jump pay.

The training was split into three segments: Ground Week, Tower Week, and Jump Week, with constant, grueling, physical activity interspersed between jump training classes. It was an intense three weeks, but John was extremely glad for the experience.

Upon graduation, John received orders for deployment to Vietnam, and then he was granted a 30-day leave before his overseas tour would begin. It felt good to be home after months of intense training and seeing his younger brothers and parents. Life felt normal for a moment. John stayed busy helping his dad and brothers complete winter chores on the ranch. The ranch work helped keep his mind off what was ahead. His dad asked a lot of questions about training and current weapons in use. Even though he did his best to hide it, John could sense an apprehension and sadness which had come over his dad.

COLD AND DANGEROUS

I'M TOO YOUNG TO BE THIS OLD

FEELS LIKE I'VE BEEN BOUGHT AND SOLD

EVERYTHING IS ON PERMANENT HOLD

CAN'T REMEMBER BEING SO COLD

CHAPTER 12
Leave

John was home on leave from the Army after finishing his Basic, Advanced Individualized Training, and Airborne Training before shipping out to Vietnam. Vietnam was a place the brothers constantly heard about from watching the nightly news and reading newspaper and magazine articles. They never envisioned that Vietnam would become such an integral part of their lives.

It felt great to be with his brothers. To say that they were close in age only would have been a huge understatement. They were both brothers and best friends. The decision to enlist and serve their country before going on with their lives was never questioned. It was just the way things were in their world.

The sun was just beginning to set upon the horizon as the brothers readied to leave for town. Someone who had never experienced such a sunset might have actually paid to see the panoramic display of Mother Nature's splendor, but the brothers hardly noticed. Their only concern was getting to town, a small community of about 50 nestled along the banks of a small creek west of the ranch.

Their destination was the local community hall which had been built decades before and was used by the local population for many functions, including wedding dances, funeral wakes, school plays, family reunions, immunizations, voting, roller skating and a monthly dance which was being held that night.

The hall was covered in textured tin and featured a tall false front which made it seem much grander than it really was. It wasn't the facility, it was the people who made the hall special, plus the fact it was the only place in town large enough to accommodate any amount of people.

The brothers had a reputation, although only local, that was legendary, and they were on their way to town to improve upon it and have some fun. Fun was whatever you could get away with without getting caught.

Like the time they snuck into old Ray's pigpen and borrowed a Hampshire piglet on the way to town. They knew Ray would be in the house passed out from spending the afternoon at the bar and wouldn't hear a thing. When they got to town, they hid their car, grabbed a flashlight, and went to the backside of the community hall. They crawled through the crawl space in the rear of the building until they were underneath the stage with the piglet, holding its mouth shut so it would not make any noise.

The hall was packed with people dancing around the crowded dance floor to the music of a country western band performing on the raised stage at the backside of the hall. There was a small access door on the underside of the stage which opened to the dance floor. The brothers opened the small access door just enough to squeeze the piglet through and release it onto the dance floor. It became a full-blown riot when the piglet hit the floor, squealing and running around among the dancing crowd.

When the crowd finally figured out what was going on, it turned into a real fracas as people tried to catch the piglet. They recognized the piglet as old Ray's because he was the only one in the county who raised Hampshire hogs, but they knew he couldn't have caused this because he would be at home passed out by now. They never did figure out for sure who was responsible, but they all had their suspicions.

Their father, although a strict disciplinarian, did not disapprove of fun. He even participated at times. "Just don't hurt or belittle anyone, don't get caught, and don't ever tell on one another or anyone else," was his advice, and their father's advice was always adhered to. This the brothers had learned through trial and error, as all boys learn.

A pact had been made for tonight's outing

which allowed for no girls. It was going to be a night for brothers only. Their first priority was refreshments. The local bar sold beer to anyone who was old enough to drive, and since the age of fourteen, when he received a learner's permit, John had purchased beer on a regular basis. It seemed as if everyone the brothers knew was at the dance, and John was upset with himself for buying beer because everyone wanted to buy one for him as a farewell gesture.

John had been gone from home for seven months, but it seemed much longer. He noticed a distinct immaturity and lack of direction in some of his former classmates, who were doing everything possible to avoid being drafted. John had been brought up believing that this was a free country, and every man was free to make his own decisions. However, he had very little respect for their actions, which they must have sensed because they all avoided any engaged conversations about Vietnam.

There were a couple of veterans there who had just returned from Vietnam. John wanted desperately to talk to them without seeming too inquisitive. The first one he approached was very drunk and only wanted trouble. Even though John knew he could take him, he was not in the mood for a fight and extracted himself from the drunken vet's presence. The second vet did not want to talk but did tell John to be careful when he heard what John's MOS (military occupational specialty) was.

John resigned himself to not be like those vets when he got back. Later that night after he had drank too much himself, he decided to look up the one who had wanted trouble and give it to him. He found the two vets in a corner. Both were too drunk to stand. One of them was crying uncontrollably and the other one appeared to be in a state of shock. John wanted to offer them help, but he had no idea where to begin.

The younger members of the community treated John like a hero even though he hadn't done anything yet but survive training. His former high school classmates were mostly trying to avoid getting drafted, which he found discouraging. He began to feel awkward and uncomfortable, and if it had not been for his brothers, the whole night would have become a very depressing event. He felt closer to his brothers than ever and wished that their lives together could go on forever. John was beginning to learn that friends can come and go, but family is forever. He was beginning to have serious doubts about where he was headed and why.

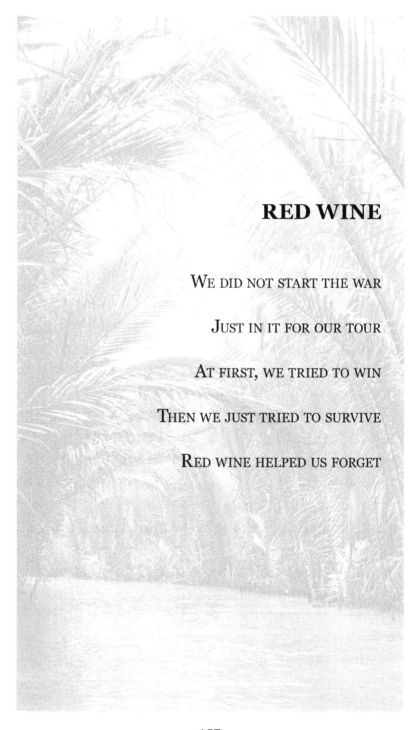

RED WINE

WE DID NOT START THE WAR

JUST IN IT FOR OUR TOUR

AT FIRST, WE TRIED TO WIN

THEN WE JUST TRIED TO SURVIVE

RED WINE HELPED US FORGET

CHAPTER 13
In Country

The day John left the ranch for Vietnam began with a grand breakfast prepared by Helen. Jay and Jake had breakfast with John before he left with his dad for the airport 125 miles east of the ranch on a cold, blustery, winter day.

Joe kept John's mind occupied during the ride talking about plans and future projects for the ranch. The roads were slick with compacted snow, and the wind was blowing snow across the highway creating visibility problems which would make navigating the highway home more difficult once it became dark. John was concerned about his dad driving home in the dark and insisted that he leave immediately for the return trip to the ranch after dropping him off at the front entrance to the airport.

Joe gave him an unexpected hug and said, "Now you be careful. Remember everything you've learned, and you will do fine."

John stood there on the sidewalk in front of the airport until his dad's car disappeared into the traffic going west. He turned around, grabbed his duffel bag, and headed into the airport to begin his journey to the military base where the processing center was located near a large city on the West Coast. He had left one day earlier than necessary because all military flights were standby, and you never knew if you were going to be on a flight or not until the last minute. John did not like traveling in uniform, but his other choice would have been paying his own way.

When his last flight landed, there were military buses waiting to transport military personnel from the airport to the military base where the processing center was located. Upon arrival at the base, they were assigned to holding barracks and not allowed to leave the area around the barracks except for the mess hall and a nearby PX store.

Converse, Big Jim, Leon, Joe, and Billy were also there along with other troops from their AIT training company. Sam was not there, and no one had seen or spoken to him since AIT training. Billy became especially concerned as they had become good friends, so he wrote Sam a letter and mailed it from the base. After he got back from mailing the letter, Leon said, "You dumb ass. How do you think you're going to get an answer when you don't even know where you're going to be in a week?"

Billy answered, "Well, at least I tried."

Converse, Big Jim, Billy, and Leon wound up on the same flight as John, and they were able to sit together. The entire Boeing 707 was packed with soldiers. John had never been on such a large airliner. It featured deluxe services, and the stewardesses saw to their every need plus they were friendly and beautiful.

A sergeant across the aisle who was headed back to Vietnam for his second tour said, "You boys enjoy those round-eyed gals while you can. You won't be seeing anything like them for a while."

The atmosphere in the airliner was boisterous, and the noise created by the troops was almost reassuring. Eventually things quieted down as people fell asleep or drifted into their own thoughts. When the plane neared Hawaii, the noise and activity increased, and they took turns looking out of the porthole-sized plane windows, marveling at the beautiful beaches and green volcanic mountains in the distance.

Everyone was in a joyful mood exiting the plane and excited to be in Hawaii. The mood quickly changed when they were placed within a chain link fenced area with MPs guarding it. Tourists moving through the airport appeared to intentionally ignore the caged troops, and it did not take long before all the troops wanted was to get back on the plane and get away from Hawaii.

Billy spoke for them all when he screamed

"Fuck you all, you bunch of assholes!" That didn't make the MPs very happy. John and Big Jim grabbed Billy and calmed him down so he wouldn't wind up in the brig before they got back on the plane.

Their next stop, Okinawa, was a barren, desolate island, but it seemed to suit the troops better, and John began to feel like his odyssey into Southeast Asia was becoming real. Immediately upon exiting the aircraft in Vietnam, the heat was the first thing John noticed. You couldn't help but be affected by it. The intense heat engulfed everything and appeared to regulate the pace of activity to a sluggish crawl. The smell was the second sense that caught John's attention. It was a stagnant, permeating smell of something unrecognizable rotting or decomposing mixed in with exhaust fumes that hung over everything like a huge, invisible cloud.

There were troops waiting to load onto the plane they had just exited. Their tours were over, and they were heading back to the world as they called home.

John could immediately distinguish the field troops from the base troops. The field troops' boots were embedded with red dust, and their uniforms were either well used and dirty or brand new, and they had hair grown well beyond military regulations. It was their actions that made them stand out even more. Their movements, hesitant and measured, heads turning, probing their surroundings, ever vigilant, with eyes constantly scanning for any out of sync detail, even though they were standing within sight of the freedom bird which would carry them back to the world.

John could only wonder what they had been through, and then he remembered his dad and how he exhibited the same behavior that John was currently viewing. He suddenly realized that he, Jay, and Jake had all indirectly learned the same behaviors from their dad, and their skills of perception of their surroundings began to make sense to John. They were not born with it, they learned it from their dad.

They were marched a short distance to an in-country processing center. John, Leon, and Billy were excited to discover that they all had been assigned to the same battalion within the division. A portion of their group was also assigned to the same division and battalion.

They were bused across the airfield and loaded onto a C-130 military transport aircraft that would fly them to their assigned battalion headquarters. The accommodations were sparse compared to the civilian aircraft. Seating was uncomfortable webbing hanging from the inside of the cargo bay walls with pallets of supplies stacked down the middle. The noise inside the bay was deafening, making communication difficult, and the ride was anything but smooth.

When the C-130 landed, they were again bused to another processing center in their new battalion. John and four other troops were pulled aside and speedily processed in, issued combat gear and weapons, then told to report to the battalion master sergeant immediately.

The master sergeant looked mean, gruff, and intimidating, but when he began to speak, it made John remember another of his dad's sayings, "Never judge a book by its cover."

The master sergeant's voice and words were calm and caring as he said, "The battalion has been engaged in a major operation for five days. Contact has been hot and heavy. Charlie Company has been hit especially hard, and they desperately need replacements. You will be flying in this evening on Huey UH-1 resupply helicopters. I could only find room enough for five of you. Be ready for immediate contact, follow orders, and trust those boys out there. They know what they're doing. You are line grunts now. May God see you through this."

John looked at the four other soldiers who were complete strangers to him and wondered if he looked and emulated fear like they did. Then he realized he had lost contact with everyone he knew and had trained with.

They were split up, three on one Huey helicopter and two on the other. The Huey helicopter that John and two other soldiers were placed on was so overloaded with ammo and supplies that it had to skip down the runway to become airborne. The crew chief gave them instructions after they were seated. He told them that they were entering a hot LZ (landing zone) and to exit immediately upon landing and do exactly as they were told by personnel on the ground. He also told them to load every magazine they carried with 18 rounds only, and they were to place a magazine into their weapons but not chamber a round until they were on the ground and received assignments.

John loaded the seven magazines he had been issued and then helped another soldier who hadn't even finished his first one. He also checked to make sure that water canteens, frag grenades, claymore mine, and other gear were secure and in place on his web gear and ruck sack. He also double-checked the three bandoleers of ammo he had been issued to make sure they were secure.

Sergeant Necco had shown John how to properly pack a ruck sack and load various web gear. John was glad for the pointers as he hastily packed back at the base. He felt as ready as he could be. The crew chief yelled to get ready to depart, and then said, "Watch me and I will signal you when to exit."

The night was pitch black when a flashing strobe suddenly appeared on the ground ahead of them. The descent was immediate and abrupt, and the landing was jarring. Both door gunners began laying down suppressing fire with the two M-60s suspended from bungee cords through the open cargo doors located on both sides of the Huey helicopter cargo area. The troops on the ground also began laying down suppressing fire as the enemy responded with a massive incoming barrage directed mostly at the Huey helicopter. It was chaotic and confusing with red tracers going out and green tracers coming in. The noise was deafening!

John could hear the Huey helicopter taking hits as he exited. A soldier came rushing up, grabbed him, and said, "You stay here and help unload the Huey!" He then directed the other two new troops to follow another soldier and do what they were told. John had never seen cargo unloaded so swiftly. The Huey helicopter then waited for priority medivacs to be brought up and loaded on board despite the intense incoming fire. John was amazed at the bravery exhibited by the Huey helicopter's crew.

"Grab all that you can carry and follow me!" was the next command John received after he had exited the Huey helicopter.

Then someone yelled, "Incoming!" and the soldier grabbed John and started pulling him into the darkness until they reached a two-man fighting hole and jumped into it as mortar rounds began impacting around them. The fighting became so intense that the second Huey helicopter was forced to wait in orbit until it ran low on fuel and had to return to base.

The soldier who had pulled John to the fighting hole introduced himself, "They call me Snake because of a snake tattoo that goes down my left arm. I got really drunk one night and woke up in the morning with this giant snake tattoo on my arm, and I've hated it ever since. My real name is Ed, but I may as well change it to Snake because of a damn tattoo." He crouched down in the bottom of the hole, leaned back, and lit a cigarette, shielding the end with one hand and said, "Shit, we'll wait for things to cool down before we go out to get the rest of the supplies. Let this be your first lesson. Always beware of a no moon night! ... Now, what is your name and where are you from back in the world?"

John introduced himself and where he was from to which Snake replied, "Where in the hell is that?"

John had to reference the nearest large city in another state before Snake could comprehend where John was from.

"Well, you are a first for me. What do you want to be called?"

John answered, "John would be fine."

Snake replied, "Well, it may be Johnny Boy until you prove yourself."

After the second Huey helicopter had to leave without delivering its supplies and the two new troops on board, a fire mission around the company's perimeter was called in, and it suppressed most of the incoming. John had never been near this much incoming artillery and was amazed at its accuracy. John mentioned this to Snake, who replied, "Yes, the company has a good FO (forward observer; fire support specialist). We just need to keep him alive."

John spent the rest of the night in the fighting hole except for a few quick trips with Snake to bring in the abandoned supplies unloaded from the Huey helicopter. Snake would come and go periodically throughout the night to check on the rest of his squad.

The next morning John and the other two new soldiers were gathered up and taken to see Lieutenant Brown, their platoon commander, to receive their squad assignments. Lieutenant Brown introduced himself and asked a few personal questions and then announced their assignments. John and one of the other new troops named Pat were assigned to Snake's squad. The other troop was sent to another squad.

When they got up to leave, Lieutenant Brown asked John to stay back. He took a long, hard look at John and asked, "Why did Snake request you? You two are as different as night and day! What did you do last night to impress him?"

John thought about it and said, "I did what I was told to do, only that."

Lieutenant Brown said, "Snake is a good squad leader, but he is a task master and won't hesitate to unload on you verbally and sometimes even physically. Just wanted to let you know that he's never requested anyone before, but don't let it go to your head. Follow his orders. You can trust him. Now go and make him trust you."

When John and Pat found Snake, he took

them over to his squad area and introduced them to the rest of the squad. Steve's resemblance to Elvis Presley was so amazing that everyone began calling him Elvis, and Elvis became his name. He was sitting on his poncho with no shirt on meticulously cleaning his M16 rifle with parts laid out neatly. He stopped to make some small talk and then continued with his cleaning task.

Pete was next. All he had on was a pair of shorts made from cutting off the legs from a pair of field pants and boots. He was full of questions and offered to help them properly pack their gear for the bush.

Pat's rucksack and web gear were a mess, and Pete went to work immediately helping him get organized while talking nonstop and asking more questions. When he got Pat organized and grabbed John's gear, he looked at it and asked, "Where did you learn how to do this? Is this your second tour?"

Rick, the last member of the squad they were introduced to, looked spent and did not say much except *welcome*, and then he leaned back against his rucksack and went to sleep.

John noticed that there were six in the squad when there should be ten. He would ask Snake about that later.

Early that afternoon Snake called the squad together and announced that they had been assigned to LP (listening post) duty for the coming night, and they were going to go out and dig a new two-man hole.

"We are not going to use an old location that Mr. Charlie has zeroed in. Word is that the gooks are beating feet toward Cambodia. But Luke the Gook will have left behind enough troops to keep us occupied and try to conceal their departure. We may be moved tomorrow to try and intercept the retreat so have your gear in order. Now, let's go dig a hole!"

Wow, John thought as he was helping dig a two-man hole in front of the company's position. *What an introduction to Vietnam, being inserted into the middle of a major firefight last night, and tonight will be spent in a two-man hole out in front of the company perimeter as a human listening post with a PRC* (backpack portable tactical radio) *as our only contact.*

Snake had chosen John and Elvis for the duty. Each platoon was required to provide two men for LP duty when it was deemed necessary. Elvis told John to gather as many grenades as he could comfortably carry secured to his web gear and to bring extra water and bug juice.

"We will bring rifles along, but our job tonight is to alert the company of any enemy activity within our area. We'll only use grenades if it gets bad! We'll have our rifles."

Later that evening they heard movement off to their left front and called it in. Shortly a voice hissed through the radio, "Heads down! You two, copy?"

"Copy," Elvis whispered back into the handset. He grabbed John and whispered, "Down! They're doing a mad minute fire drill into our area."

John could not believe the barrage of tracers that were passing over them. They became so intense that they created an eerie glow down into their hole.

"Neat, huh?" laughed Elvis.

The rest of the night was uneventful except for the mosquitos. John had never experienced anything as miserable as the endless hordes of mosquitos, and he had used up both of his insect repellent squeeze bottles halfway through the night. Elvis said, "I brought along extra bottles for you but was only going to give them to you if I liked you. You ain't been too bad so far, so here's some more bug juice. Also, because you are not too bad of a guy, I'll give you one more tip. Get rid of the boxer shorts. Once we start marching, they'll rub you so raw it'll hurt even standing still. Keep one pair to wear as shorts if you want to, but don't wear them under your jungle pants."

Snake was right, and early the next day, the company was ordered to police up their areas and burn anything that could be reused by the enemy.

"It's going to be a lovely hike into the mountains, so secure all gear properly. Our platoon will be on morning point for today's march. We will rotate point man every two hours. Get ready to move in one hour."

Rick spoke up, "Do they really expect us to

catch up with them?"

Snake answered, "Rick, you know the drill, so let's follow our orders and do the best we can."

The chase through the mountainous jungle was an extraordinary experience for John, and after a few days, he was already beginning to feel comfortable. He found himself learning at every step, and his uncanny ability to recognize anything out of the ordinary helped identify booby traps set along a trail. Sergeant Necco's training was proving to be invaluable.

The company spent four days pursuing the retreating North Vietnamese unit and repeatedly encountered resistance by squads of North Vietnamese and Viet Cong soldiers emplaced strategically along their path of retreat and numerous booby traps set on trails to slow their pursuit. After the fourth day the company turned around and headed back to the hill where the encounter had begun.

John's legendary status began late in the afternoon on the third day of the pursuit when the company suddenly came to a halt at the edge of a large field of elephant grass. To cross it, they would be completely exposed. A large vertical cliff bordered one side, and the other side was a deep ravine that featured a raging mountain stream at its bottom. On the other side of the field about a half click away was a towering wall of jungle.

The retreating enemy troops had left an inviting trail through the center of the field. The company's captain was concerned because it was a perfect setup for an ambush. Word had spread fast through the company about John's uncanny ability to distinguish anything out of the ordinary. The captain had him called forward to see if the rumors were real, and the field was making him nervous.

When John reached the command group at the edge of the field, he asked the FO if he could borrow his binoculars, and he began glassing across the field into the triple canopy jungle. Almost immediately he spotted a sniper's nest in a tree. Captain Evan was incredulous. They had just spent the last half hour peering into the jungle on the other side of the field and hadn't noticed anything.

John said, "That's not the end of it. I think there's a mortar team over there near the ravine."

Captain Evan asked John for the binoculars and began peering into the jungle near the ravine, and said, "I can't see anything to suggest that!"

John explained the irregularities in the vegetation. Captain Evan again peered through the binoculars, and said, "I see what you are pointing out. If you are right, private, what do you suggest we do?"

John said, "First, I would do a mad minute into that tree with the sniper and then bring up all of the M79s and LAWs (light anti-armor weapons) you've got and blow their mortar team off that cliff!"

Captain Evan again scanned the tree with the sniper in it and asked, "Are you sure about the sniper?"

John answered, "Positive, I am surprised he hasn't shot yet!"

This caused the captain and everyone else in the command group to drop down. The captain growled, "Get all grenadiers and LAWs up front now, and have one squad do a mad minute fire drill into that damn tree now."

About halfway through the mad minute, a sniper fell from the tree, got up, and started running into the jungle. He then turned around and ran back looking for his rifle which he'd dropped as he fell. The squad opened up on him now that they had a visible target, and the sniper fell backwards for good.

Captain Evan said, "I'll be damned."

Then the M79 grenadiers and a handful of troops with LAW rockets came forward and were directed where to fire. The captain also ordered the squad to direct another mad minute into the mortar nest at the same time. Small, secondary explosions and cries for help from the position confirmed that John had been spot on.

Captain Evan took a long, hard look at John then asked, "Son, where are you from and how did you do this?"

When John told the captain where he was from, Captain Evans blurted out, "Are you part Indian?"

"No," John said, "but I have friends who are. A training NCO back in AIT told me how his platoon was ambushed in a similar situation. The outcome wasn't good, so that's what I looked for, snipers and mortar teams. I guess that I just got lucky."

The captain said, "Private, you have a special gift, and I'm glad that you're on our side!" Then he barked out, "Bring 'em up and move 'em across one platoon at a time and stay off the trail the gooks left!"

He looked over at John and said, "Private, will you take point for a while when we get across?"

John answered, "I certainly would but my squad needs a break. We were on point most of this morning."

The captain said, "We can fix that. You just get us started in case there are any booby traps waiting for us on the other side of this damn field!"

That evening the captain's radio operator came over to their squad area and said, "Captain Evan wants to speak to you."

John followed him back to the command center. Captain Evan looked up and said, "Private, I was amazed by your actions today and want you on point whenever the company is moving."

John stood still while analyzing the request before answering. "Impossible, I can't do that," he said.

Captain Evan asked, "Why is that impossible?"

John answered, "When we're on patrol, walking point is the most dangerous position in the company. No one I know would have the mental stamina to stay totally focused for an assignment like that."

Captain Evan sat there, staring at John. He finally said, "I never thought of it that way. Can I put you on call to walk point if I deem it necessary for the safety of the company?"

John replied, "Only if my squad isn't assigned to walk point for the day."

Captain Evan paused again. He finally agreed to John's terms and then dismissed him. As John was walking away, Captain Evan said, "Thank you for today, private."

When John returned to his squad, Snake immediately asked, "What was that about?"

John explained the captain's request and Snake said, "I knew you were special the moment I met you. We're going to miss you in our squad."

John told Snake that he had turned down the captain's request and why, then he assured Snake that he was still a part of his squad.

The North Vietnamese soldiers and Viet Cong guerrillas were masters at selecting ambush sites and initially gaining the upper hand in a battle. John soon became an expert at recognizing an ambush site. The enemy was cunning, but there was a familiarity to their selection of ambush sites and set ups, plus there were very subtle clues. There was no way they could dig bunkers and trenches, cut and move trees, and pull branches and other plants down for concealment without leaving evidence of the disturbance no matter how minor. All these clues stood out to John so much that he could sense the enemy's presence, and he saved the company from entering an ambush site more than once.

Before John left for Vietnam, his dad had sat him down and explained how the Japanese set up ambush sites and what to look for. Joe's advice helped John tremendously with understanding subtle clues left behind from creating an ambush site.

Early one morning while John was on point, he caught a whiff of something that was different from the jungle odors surrounding him. He froze, focusing with all his senses on high alert. The scent had disappeared as quickly as it had appeared. John stood perfectly still for a few minutes but couldn't detect the odor again. He moved back to the command group for a conference.

John told Captain Evans that he wanted to do a recon to their south to see if he could discover the source of something he'd smelled. Captain Evans agreed, but he insisted that John take someone along for backup. Snake volunteered.

They dropped their packs and shouldered one bandolier of ammo. After moving south for 90 meters, John and Snake both noticed the smell. They instantly recognized it as human waste. They stealthily moved toward the odor and eventually discovered a straddle trench with a large amount of human waste in it. They were moving back toward the waiting company when John suddenly stopped. Using hand gestures, he directed Snake to stay in place while he reconned a slightly elevated ridge line he'd noticed nearby that was parallel to their company's route of march. John backed away immediately when he spotted the backside of a concealed enemy bunker.

Snake and John cautiously moved back to the company command group. They reported to Captain Evans that the company was about to enter an L-shaped ambush which they estimated was manned by at least a platoon, maybe even a company-sized enemy force.

Maps were pulled out, the FO plotted for artillery with John and Snake's assistance while Captain Evans and the platoon lieutenants formulated a counterattack. It turned out to be a company of regular force NVA (North Vietnamese Army) who eventually tried to break contact and escape but where overwhelmed by a superbly executed counterattack and effective artillery strikes.

A battle fought by a company-sized unit was like a ballet of organized chaos. The noise was deafening with the smell of gunpowder permeating the air. Squad leaders were constantly barking orders while platoon lieutenants and the company's captain were screaming into PRC-25 radio handsets directing troops and calling in for artillery or air support if it was deemed necessary. Incoming rounds tore through trees and other foliage creating hundreds of snapping sounds. Sometimes the foliage rained down like confetti. The amount of ammo expended in the first few minutes was amazing.

So far John's company had only been in engagements with squad, platoon, and company-sized enemy units, and he was glad for that. A division-sized enemy unit with emplaced 12.7 heavy machine guns was something he did not want to encounter. Their RPD machine guns (portable machine guns that fired 7.62 x 51 mm bullets) caused enough havoc, but a 12.7 could literally cut down trees. John knew that it would only be a matter of time before they encountered an enemy division and would have to face not only bunkered 12.7s and RPD machine guns but emplaced mortar squads and roving RPG (shoulder-fired rocket launcher that fired a B40 rocket) teams.

Explosive booby traps were another terrifying aspect of moving a company through the bush. John was constantly trying to train fellow squad members how to detect booby traps. He just couldn't give them the ability to stay constantly focused.

Despite their unprofessional appearances and lackluster attitudes toward military protocol, the company's troops always came forward and fought hard, sacrificing their own safety to assist each other. After a couple of months serving as a line grunt, John received orders to report back to the unit's base camp. He was being reassigned to a LRRP unit (pronounced *lurp*; Long-Range Reconnaissance Patrol) within the infantry division he was assigned to. John had no idea what a LRRP unit was, and the first person he asked said, "Man, you are going to live in Indian country. Good luck!"

What John eventually found out about the LRRPs excited him immensely. The LRRPs sounded like what he had been made for. Their primary missions were long range reconnaissance patrols that could last up to six days. Secondary missions were bomb damage assessments, small ambushes, and occasionally a downed pilot recovery. They were comprised of six-man teams, and his division had a separate company of them.

John had mixed feelings about leaving his squad. It was hard saying goodbye. They had bonded, and he felt he was deserting them.

Snake set him straight. "I knew you were meant for greater things. You will be a huge asset to the Army as a LRRP. We'll miss you for sure, but you've helped me and the squad more than you'll ever realize. Now go do what you do best."

John was impressed with the people he encountered upon entering the LRRP company area, and he felt accepted when he was introduced to his team leader and the rest of the team he'd been assigned to. But John knew that he would have to earn the team's trust. His dad once told him that actions always speaks louder than words.

John's team leader was a small, intense guy

with a shaved head called Spike. He was from South Carolina and had a lot of questions about snow and extreme cold when he discovered where John was from. He found it hard to believe that people lived under those harsh conditions.

Spike was a good leader who was serious about his responsibility as a team leader and meticulous about everything. The other four men included a tall, light-haired guy named Scotty from Florida who could tell jokes all night if he wanted to. John was amazed with Scotty's ability to always see a humorous side to stressful moments they encountered.

Next was Rick, a college dropout who was extremely serious and observant. He helped John secure the proper LRRP patrol gear and arrange it for efficiency.

Spike said, "Nothing gets by Rick. Trust his instincts and you will be fine."

The third team member was called Judd. He was a huge, imposing guy from Texas who was like an overprotective big brother always watching out for his fellow team members and steady as a rock in battle.

Then there was Obie from Nebraska, who became John's best friend almost immediately, for starters they both grew up on ranches and liked horses. Spike told John that Obie was fearless and totally controlled in a firefight, and he could always be counted on to inflict the most damage to an enemy unit.

John was also introduced to the CAR-15 which was the weapon of choice for LRRPs. Judd carried an M79 grenade launcher which he was quite effective with. He primarily used 40mm HE rounds but also carried WP and airburst rounds plus buckshot and flechette rounds for close range.

Judd always carried more than the standard load of ammo for his M79. Everyone in the team always packed a few more HE rounds into their rucks for Judd, which he appreciated.

They began their bonding with John almost immediately with a case of warm Schmidt beer secured earlier from the NCO club on base and continued until the beer was gone. The leadership within the entire unit impressed John, and he always felt safer in the bush with a six-man team than in his previous tenure as a line grunt with an entire company in tow. One of the reasons was the leadership exhibited by his superiors. Command and control oversaw the missions but allowed the team leaders to make split second decisions if conditions on the ground dictated to ensure the team's safety and the mission's completion. Any other mission deviations were communicated to command and control by team leaders and discussed before being implemented. One day Spike told John to not get too spoiled because command rotated out about every six months, and things could change.

John's favorite position was walking point. He liked being up front with all his senses functioning at their maximum ability, searching for clues of an impending ambush or booby traps. His perceptive skills were keen and instantaneous. A smell, unnatural sound, damaged or out of place foliage, unnatural wildlife behavior, or an abrupt change in the form and texture of the landscape all gave John clues, sometimes simultaneously, that were processed and categorized instantly. Time seemed to stand still and fly by at the same time.

He excelled as a LRRP and knew he had trained all his life for this. John had been in country for a little over eight months when Jay arrived. He was assigned to a different infantry division as a company line grunt, just as John had initially been.

John had written Jay while he was still in his advanced individualized training and told him to request an assignment to a LRRP company immediately after his arrival in Vietnam, but the Army did not operate like that. They put you where they wanted when they wanted. John went up the divisional ladder within his unit as far as he could and asked them to contact Jay's division to see if anything could be done to reassign Jay to a LRRP unit within their division.

John pleaded with them, "We were both made for this! We've trained for this all our lives. Jay will be one of the best LRRPs they've ever seen, guaranteed!"

John knew he was in a good unit when he was

informed that contact had been made within Jay's divisional unit, and Jay would likely be transferred to their LRRP company when a position became available. Nothing was guaranteed, but it was great news. John immediately wrote Jay encouraging him to hang in there. Life would be getting better.

Jay's company had also discovered his skills, and walking point became Jay's only duty while they were on patrol. It appeared to John from Jay's letters that his company was not rotating their point personnel, and Jay was being kept on point duty for extended periods without breaks.

John knew from experience that walking point required constant mental clarity, and if done for extended periods for days on end, no one could possibly maintain the proper focus continually for the most dangerous job assignment on a patrol. John became concerned about his younger brother's safety and found it hard waiting for Jay to be transferred to a LRRP unit. He tried to be positive and hide his concerns in his letters to Jay.

He knew something was amiss when his team exited the helicopter back at base camp after completing a four-day mission. The company commander and a chaplain were standing by a Jeep waiting for the team. John wondered who they were waiting for, probably with bad news for someone from the team about a family member from home.

When he saw them zero in on him, he froze.

He just couldn't take another step. No, not Jay! It couldn't be! Jay was too good of a soldier!

When the chaplain and colonel walked up to John, he shouted out, "This better not be about Jay!"

They informed him that Jay had been killed by a concealed, hand-detonated land mine, and he was being assigned as the official military escort for Jay's body which was being flown home on the next available airline transport for a military burial.

At the funeral John's dad and younger brother were stoic and supportive. His mother couldn't stop crying and clung onto John tenaciously. The next day John's dad wanted all the details, and John told him all that he was able to gather in a short time from secondhand sources. He also gave him the names of people to contact in Jay's platoon who were there when the event occurred and could answer his questions directly. John also informed his dad of his suspicions from the letters Jay had sent him in country.

John's dad's face became very stern as he said, "I'll take care of this."

That's all he had said, and John later learned through the grapevine that he apparently had and very swiftly. Heads had rolled in Jay's unit with the help of two state senators, one who had occasionally hunted on the ranch with their dad. Jake later wrote John and told him that their dad had contacted the senators requesting their help.

Joe, Helen, and Jake all came along to see John's departure back to Vietnam after the funeral. Helen did not want to let go of him at the airport, and he thought he might miss the plane. She finally let go of him and said, "Please be safe."

It was the saddest he had ever seen her. He remembered looking at his younger brother Jake and seeing revenge all over his face and saying, "Don't do this!" but he knew Jake couldn't be stopped just like he couldn't.

On the flight back to Vietnam, John couldn't stop thinking of Jay. What more could he have done to protect him? He had written Jay explaining the request his company captain had made for him to walk point continuously while the company was on the move. John also shared with Jay how he'd responded to that request. Deep down, John knew that Jay was partially at fault. Jay had always been fearless and pushed himself to the limit no matter what the odds were. The more dangerous and challenging something was, the more he seemed to crave it.

John finally concluded that he and his brothers were not invincible despite their gifts of perception and training. He vowed to keep his head on straight so he would be there for Jake. He finally fell asleep and didn't wake up until the plane began its descent. He looked out the window and thought to himself, *I've got to get through the next 60 days so I can be there for Jake.*

COMING HOME

THERE ARE MOMENTS WHEN NOTHING IS WORSE

THAN BEING WITH PEOPLE WHO CANNOT COMPREHEND

OR REALLY DO NOT CARE TO UNDERSTAND WAR

CHAPTER 14
The Odyssey Continues

John arrived back in country from the most difficult military assignment he had ever performed, escorting Jay's body back to the United States for burial. Spike silently questioned if John would be able to stay totally focused on his job in the bush. He was concerned about the team's safety, so he kept John busy assisting teams preparing for missions but refused to let him go out on any missions so soon after returning from the burial of his younger brother.

When John discovered an ambush mission was being planned, he immediately requested to be assigned to the 12-man heavy team going in. Spike refused the request. He knew that John had been on the team which had discovered the high-speed trail where the mission would take place. John would be a great asset to the 12-man heavy team on the mission, but Spike was hesitant.

John was so persistent that Spike finally relented with a warning, "I'll pull you out instantly if I see anything out of the ordinary."

John was thankful to be a part of the heavy team. It helped take his mind off Jay, and he made sure to thank Spike at every opportunity. He kept busy helping the two team leaders prepare for the mission and spent many hours with them reviewing topo maps of the AO (geographically defined area of operation) to identify possible insertion and extraction sites and routes of travel to the ambush site.

They were going to have two full artillery batteries of 105mm and 155mm howitzers at their disposal, and they did artillery preplots around the ambush site. They would also do artillery preplots of the insertion and extraction sites when they selected them after an overflight of the AO. The evening before the mission, John double-checked his weapons, ammo, grenades, claymore mines, and all the various combat equipment attached to his LBE (load-bearing equipment harness for combat gear) and stashed into his ruck. John was totally focused on the mission and anxious for it to begin.

The next day the team was inserted at first light. To confuse any enemy soldiers in the vicinity, the Huey helicopters did two false insertions before they went directly to the selected insertion site. After quickly exiting the helicopters, the team moved 50 meters into the double canopy jungle.

Their RTO did a commo check and the first sitrep (situation report called in at predetermined schedule) of the day. After that, they laid dog for 30 minutes in a wagon wheel formation before moving out.

John had traversed through this area recently and took point, leading the team toward the ambush site. They pushed hard through the double and triple canopy jungle, stopping at noon to call in the second sitrep of the day. Even with limited lines of sight, by using his compass and topo maps, John was able to keep the team moving close to the preplotted route of march.

They were halfway to the ambush location when they found a good spot to lay up for the night. The mission had gone well so far, but everyone was on edge because this was an ambush mission. There were a lot of things that could go wrong with an ambush. Being at double strength concealment was another concern as 12 men were harder to move and conceal even in the bush.

They did a recon around their night lair, then held a team briefing of the escape and evasion route. The RTO called in the final sitrep of the day, meals were eaten, and then the team set out claymore mines and laid up in a defensive circle at 50 percent alert for the night.

John's two-hour watch was over, but he knew that he would be unable to sleep or even rest just yet, so he didn't bother waking the lurp lying next to him. His senses were totally immersed into the night's various smells and sounds. He had been at this so long that he was totally familiar with regional wildlife and the various sounds they either emitted or created by movement. Wildlife and even certain insects had various warning signals that were invaluable if you understood them. It was like having hundreds of sentries surrounding the teams for the night.

John remembered voicing concerns to his dad one evening. "It's all jungle over there. I'm from the open prairie. How will I be able to function in a jungle?"

His dad had looked at him and calmly stated, "Land is land and animals are animals. You'll have an adjustment period. Just use what you've learned, and you'll do just fine." His dad's wisdom always amazed him.

After an uneventful night, two team members performed a recon around their night lair. Then after a meal of cold C-Rations, a team briefing, and map checks by the team leaders, the first sitrep of the day was called in by the RTO, and the teams packed up and moved out.

The plan was to move in near the ambush site, recon it, set up for another night, and then move into position early the following morning for the ambush. They hoped that the intel was correct and the targeted senior NVA commander would show up in the morning with his escort platoon heading back to Cambodia, otherwise they would have to stay in position for another day and night.

Most of the team members felt this was a long shot mission based on sketchy intel, but they had orders and would do their best. The team soon found an old trail that looked unused. After a short conference and map check, it was decided to use the trail which ran parallel to their planned route of travel. It would save time and enable them to give the team a much-needed break.

They were just about to stop for the noon sitrep when the point man began firing. He had come around a corner in the trail, and run into what appeared to be a squad of NVA soldiers moving up the trail. His quick reaction resulted in two dead enemy soldiers and a couple of blood trails. The rest of the enemy squad had escaped.

The encounter had compromised the mission. They began to suspect that the intel may have been correct because the NVA squad they'd encountered was scouting an unused trail. They also suspected that there could be other squads out pre-scouting the route. The main consensus was that Mr. Charlie would soon be hunting for the team in force, and after a short conference with the team leaders, they decided to have the RTO call for an extraction.

The team immediately began moving toward the primary prearranged extraction point. They moved as fast as they could to avoid the incoming NVA and had to lay dog once when they heard another squad of NVA patrolling near their route.

They were almost at the extraction point when they began taking heavy fire.

The NVA must have picked up their trail and were moving in with a vengeance. The 12-man team was able to hold them at bay, but the team leaders knew they would need assistance soon to avoid being overrun.

They had preplotted the extraction location, and after a quick map review and compass check, the team leaders adjusted the preplotted coordinates toward the incoming NVA. The RTO called the 105mm artillery battery for a single round of HE with the new coordinates. The round impacted exactly where they had plotted it. Then they directed the FDO (fire direction officer for artillery battery) to adjust fire on their command as they spread the artillery rounds across the incoming NVA.

At the same time, the second team leader contacted the 155mm battery and directed their fire further back toward any more incoming NVA troops. After the artillery batteries had fired nonstop volleys into the NVA positions, the incoming fire slowed down considerably.

A pink team of one LOH-6 helicopter and two Cobra gunships in the area came up on the net and offered to come in and provide additional cover for their extraction. The artillery was put on hold as the pink team came in and finished the job the artillery batteries had begun.

The artillery rounds had killed numerous

NVA troops, and the pink team killed many more survivors trying to escape. It was not a good day for the NVA. As the team loaded onto the extraction Hueys, they knew that luck had been on their side and extracting immediately had saved the team.

On the flight back to base camp, John thought back to his first mission as a lurp. They were inserted into the aftermath of a B-52 arc light bombing run to do a damage assessment. He had never seen such carnage. The run must have been right on target and appeared to have annihilated the majority of an NVA company near the Cambodian border. The 500 and 750-pound bombs had blown huge craters down the center of a mountain valley, the ground still smoldering. Everything for a click in length by one half click wide was totally obliterated. Body parts were scattered everywhere with pieces of intestines hanging from bare trees that had been stripped of their foliage. Stark white bones were strewn about or sticking up out of the ground like they had been driven into it and some were even eerily intact. Most of the bodies had been literally pulverized, and all that remained was a pink slime covering everything.

After reconning the area, the team was covered in the slime. You couldn't avoid walking in it, and anything touched was covered in it. If you slipped and fell, which was difficult to avoid while climbing over downed jungle foliage and up and down the huge craters, you became covered in the slime. Pieces of damaged weapons and equipment were scattered about, and the area had a distinct smell of death which was hard to ignore.

It was impossible to compute a body count as only a few bodies were found partially intact on the perimeter of the area, but command demanded a body count and any enemy documents. No documents were found. There were a few scraps of clothing with patches on them and some pieces of damaged equipment and weapons the team carried back with them.

After reconning the area, they gathered at the far southern edge of the first crater. After a conference, they called in a number equal to 80 percent of a company's personnel. They had arrived shortly after the bombing run and knew that there were survivors who would eventually return. The intel indicated there was a division of NVA in the area. The NVA would soon be sending in troops to find survivors, bury the dead, and salvage equipment. They called in for an immediate extraction.

When John looked back down into the valley from the extraction helicopter, chills ran up and down his spine and he began shivering uncontrollably as he thought of what it must have been like to be hit with such force without an inclination or warning. One moment life was normal, and then, in an instant, it was gone or changed forever.

As soon as they arrived back at base, they headed for the motor pool and borrowed some high-pressure washers. They laid out their gear and weapons on some aircraft landing decking, then stripped off their jungle uniforms and power washed everything to get rid of the pink slime.

Then showers were next, and true to course, Scotty began belting out a chorus that related to the day's experience. "Oh, Mr. Charlie. He disappeared today, right in front of me, never saw it coming. Now part of him is laying in a hole, while I flush the rest of him down the drain."

Scotty repeated the verses until he was thrown out of the shower by the rest of the team. After showering, their attention was turned toward their weapons and gear. It turned out to be an awfully long and grueling day for John's first assignment as a lurp.

Later into the flight back, John also began to realize that the end of his tour was nearing, and despite everything, he would miss certain aspects of his tour. Number one was his teammates in the lurp unit and back in the infantry company he'd served in. They were his heroes and the only people on earth who really knew what they'd experienced together. It would be hard if not impossible to describe certain events to someone unfamiliar with war. You just had to be there to know.

John knew a lot of his memories from the war would never and could never be shared. Like his father, they would remain his and only his, and they would end only when he did.

He would miss the adrenaline rush of insertions by helicopter. He never totally trusted them, and getting off a helicopter was the only part of flying in one that he looked forward to. He preferred being on the ground in the jungle, even with all its impending dangers, hunting an enemy that would kill you in an instant. He would not miss flying in a helicopter. He would miss lying in a circle all night in the jungle with six other men you totally trusted. But John knew that walking point was what he would miss the most. As odd as it seemed, it was the one place where he felt totally secure.

John went on a few more missions after that. They were all standard reconnaissance missions and were completed successfully and uneventful for the most part. Then his tour in Vietnam was over. He still had about five months to serve back in the states before his discharge, but he had survived.

On the freedom flight home, he kept reflecting on Sergeant Necco's words, "Be extremely cautious. Take care of the man next to you and survive. That will be your win."

R & R

Only right now counts

And it's all right now

CHAPTER 15
Jake

After returning stateside, John received orders that would put him right back where his military odyssey had begun, only this time, he wouldn't be the new recruit. He was being assigned as a training NCO (non-commissioned officer within a base training unit).

John was given a 30-day leave and a date to report for duty. He missed his brother Jay, but his mom, dad, and Jake along with the ranch kept him occupied, and the leave rejuvenated him even though it ended too early.

While he was on leave, John started teaching Jake about Mr. Charlie. He even set up fake booby traps on the ranch river bottoms and had Jake do the same drills Sergeant Necco had him do. Jake quickly became good at detecting booby traps. John wasn't too surprised. Jake had always been a better stalker than Jay or him.

After he left the ranch to finish out his military obligation, John realized he was anxious to begin his new assignment and vowed to teach the recruits everything he knew to help them achieve their *win*, as Sergeant Necco called it. After arriving at the training base, John began the seemingly endless processing-in procedures. John had to remind himself that this was typical of all Army units, and then he realized he would have to endure it only once more while being out-processed which made him feel better.

After he was done with the battalion processing, he was given a ride in a Jeep to his training company, where there was more processing-in awaiting him at the company level. John was assigned to a basic training company. His direct superior, Drill Sergeant Lucas, impressed him immediately, and when he was introduced to the other training NCOs, he felt the last five months of his tour would be productive and even enjoyable working with the training team he was assigned to. John could not believe how young the new recruits looked. Even though he was the same age as most of them, he felt much older.

Sergeant Lucas led by example, and he insisted that all his training NCOs do the same. It was an easy fit for John. He enjoyed training new recruits. There were some recruits who required extra discipline and some who needed extra training, especially with weapons.

John eventually earned their respect and followed Sergeant Necco's path by offering additional training identifying booby traps to a few select trainees who were interested. He stayed and performed the additional training after the days traditional training was over. It made him feel good to know that the knowledge he was able to give them might save their lives when they got to Vietnam. His only request was that they pass it on to the other members of their squad.

Sergeant Lucas, who kept a very watchful eye on everything and did not like deviations from training protocol, came to one of John's after-hours training classes and met with John after the class. John thought this would be the end of his classes. Sergeant Lucas admitted that he was going to call an end to the extra training. After viewing it in person, however, he admitted to John that his training should become a part of their standard training, but it would never be approved by upper brass. He told John that he could continue, but to limit his class numbers to no more than two and to keep it quiet, as it would be his ass that would be chewed on if anyone higher up discovered the classes.

John also kept communicating with Jake by mail trying to pass on everything he knew about the enemy that Jake would eventually be facing. Jake was appreciative for the information and came up with questions and issues that John had never thought of. *Little smart-ass,* John thought one day as he was responding to a question of Jake's. *Jake has always been a perfectionist, and where he's going that's not a bad thing, especially if he can get assigned to a LRRP unit.*

John's military odyssey ended almost uneventfully, and he was able to get home in time to see Jake before he left for basic training. After Jake had completed basic and advanced individual training and received orders for deployment to Vietnam, he was able to come home for leave before reporting for duty. The entire month was a whirlwind of activity! John wanted to make sure that Jake had time for Helen, Joe, and Shirley so he didn't offer any training unless Jake brought it up.

The month felt like it was over in a few days, but the bond between John and Jake became stronger as they both prepared for their futures. John tried to hide his apprehension just as his dad and mother were doing. It was hard for John, but even harder for Joe and Helen, to see Jake leaving for Vietnam. They savored every minute with Jake and let him know how loved he was.

Joe and Helen said their goodbyes at the ranch, and John drove Jake to the airport. After Jake's flight left, John continued traveling east for a short vacation to Minneapolis to visit his Aunt Anna, Uncle Ricardo, and cousins, Danny and Dennis.

That's where John was when Jake called him after he had been processed in with the news that he would be taking an in-country recon class when he arrived in Vietnam and then be assigned to a LRRP unit. John was relieved and grateful. He began to suspect that strings had been pulled, probably by a certain senator. He wanted to call his dad immediately and thank him, but he waited until a Tuesday, when his mom was gone. If she was home, Joe would not speak on a phone. He would let whoever was calling inform Helen about what they were calling for and then she would transfer it to him verbally. If it was a question, she would blurt it out to him, then he would answer, and she would relay it to the caller.

Helen hated taking Joe's calls and would answer for him at times without consulting him first which irritated him. She would inform him after the call that if he did not like her response or answer, he could start taking his own calls. It was a real hassle to call dad when mom was home.

Helen had started going to town every Tuesday, weather permitting. She would stop in and visit with old neighbors and other friends and then go shopping for groceries. She would sometimes forget that she did not have three growing boys at home to feed and overbuy groceries. All Joe would do is shake his head.

John called at noon on Tuesday because he knew his dad would be in the house for lunch and relaxing a bit from spending the morning outside taking care of livestock. He hoped his dad would answer the phone despite his dislike of talking on them. John had to let the phone ring for an extended period before his dad finally answered.

When he expressed gratitude to his dad for getting Jake assigned to a lurp unit, his dad thanked him for the good news but denied any involvement. After the call, John felt somewhat bewildered by his dad's response. Then he remembered another of his dad's proverbs—some things are better off not being said.

John was back on the ranch from his trip to Minneapolis. It was an abnormally warm winter day, and Joe and John had decided to spend the morning repairing some of the haying equipment to ready it for haying next summer. After lunch, they were going into town for cattle feed. About mid-morning Joe said he was tired and went to the house and sat on the front deck overlooking the river bottoms.

When John came to the house later for lunch, Helen told him that something was bothering his dad. She had taken coffee out to him and asked how he was feeling. All he said was, "I'm a little tired. It's nothing. All I need is some rest and this coffee."

Helen said, "I know your dad better than that. It's like he's sitting there waiting for something."

Suddenly, Joe started screaming for Helen to come out to the porch. Helen and John both ran out to the front porch. Joe was standing up staring down into the river bottoms. When he saw Helen, he wrapped his arms around her, and they both began crying.

John looked down into the river bottoms and

saw it immediately, a green military car coming down the road that sliced through the bottoms toward the ranch. John knew instantly that Jake was in trouble. He hoped for news like Jake was missing in action or had suffered a serious injury. Looking over at his parents, John knew Jake was gone. They had been through this once already.

John left the deck and met the military car in the yard. A military chaplain and an army officer got out of the car, introduced themselves, and explained to John that they were from an army casualty assistance and notification unit, and they needed to speak with Joe and Helen O'Janon.

John asked them to make this as short as possible for his parents, "Just tell them if he is dead or alive, then we'll come back here and take care of the rest."

The chaplain and officer weren't very happy with breaking their military protocol, but they finally agreed to John's request and went onto the deck. They greeted Joe and Helen and informed them that Jake had died while serving his country. Helen and Joe sat down, hugging each other, oblivious to the rest of the world. John followed the chaplain and officer back to their car where they went over burial and assistance programs available to fallen soldiers' families. John barely heard a word they were saying, then finally he interrupted them. "Just tell me how Jake died and give me a phone number to call for the burial and assistance programs?"

Jake was being flown into a LZ (landing zone) on a Huey UH-1 helicopter when it experienced mechanical issues and crashed, killing everyone on board. He had been in Vietnam a total of 35 days, and it was his first mission.

John could not comprehend how his dad knew. Was there a bond that strong between parents and their children? All he wanted to do was get away and be alone, to think things through, but he knew he needed to be there for his parents. His presence right now was important for them. He grieved with them and then stayed up with them late into the evening making funeral plans.

After Jake's funeral services and burial, everyone gathered at the local community hall for a lunch that had been prepared by neighborhood friends of the family. John had noticed how distraught Shirley was during the burial, and when he approached her to offer support, she unloaded her feelings on him.

"Damn you brothers! You could all have gone to college on athletic scholarships. This is all your fault, John! You could have done the right thing by going to college instead of that damn war and set the right path for your brothers to follow."

John could offer no response, and he knew he needed to leave. He needed to be alone. When he got home, he changed and left for a walk across the prairie to the cemetery four miles from the ranch. Right now, he needed to be near his brothers.

Almost every step brought back a memory. John looked over and saw Jay's Draw, which they'd named after Jay shot his first deer there. It had been a cold, blustery, late fall day with a couple of feet of snow on the ground. Jake had spotted them first, mule deer entering a tree-filled draw three quarters of a mile away. They waited motionless until the deer disappeared into the draw, then began moving toward the draw on the opposite side of a huge hay field stopping frequently to glass the draw because they were completely out in the open while crossing the hay field. When they reached the bottom of a butte that would give them a bird's eye view into the draw from its crest, Jake, who was too young yet for a deer license, stayed behind and John and Jay began the ascent.

John had gotten his deer the day before, so today was Jay's hunt. He was carrying the old 30-06 sporterized Mauser. They had covered the muzzle of the rifle with electrical tape that morning just for a situation like the one they were in. Even with John clearing a path through the snow for Jay, it would have been impossible for him to keep snow out of the rifle's barrel. It was an old trick Uncle Hugo had taught them when he gave the Mauser to them.

As they neared the crest of the butte, they dropped down on their hands and knees and eventually began low crawling through the snow. John remembered how cold he got crawling through the snow which was filtering into his clothes. There was more snow inside his clothes than outside, but he continued inching forward, opening a path for Jay to follow.

John froze in place when he spotted the tops of a buck's antlers and he inched backwards. He knew that the snow was too deep for Jay to brace the rifle on his elbows for the shot, so he rolled over and slowly pulled up his knees as elevated braces and spread out his arms to signal Jay that there was a buck ahead. Then he pointed at his knees. Jay understood instantly and crawled forward slowly. He raised the rifle up and placed it over John's knees while pulling himself up onto his own knees then braced his elbows on John's knees and cycled the action to load a round into the chamber. Once he stopped moving, John began shivering and couldn't control it, but Jay didn't seem to notice and calmly took aim and fired. It was the largest mule deer buck that the brothers had ever seen, and the biggest deer taken from their neighborhood that season.

As John continued hiking toward the cemetery, he looked to his left and realized he was next to Jake's Hill which is what the brothers had named the hill after a sharp-tailed grouse hunt one fall. The hill had a snowberry patch growing about halfway up on its south side. Jake, who was carrying a single shot Stevens 20-gauge shotgun, had decided to hike up and see if any grouse were hiding in the patch. Jay told him that he was just wasting time, but Jake hiked up to the patch. As he entered it from the bottom, a coyote exited the patch from its top edge at a dead run going straight up toward the hill's crest about 60 yards away. The incident had only taken mere seconds, and Jay and John began laughing so hard that they wound up on the ground rolling over.

Jake had fired instantly and hit the coyote who was pushed downwards as if an invisible hand had pushed on his back causing him to pause for a split second, but he recovered and kept running up. Jake broke the shotgun open, pulled the empty shell out, and dropped another shell into the shotgun. He slammed it shut, then brought it up to his shoulder and shot a second time, hitting the coyote who was again pushed downwards for a split second but kept on running up. Jake reloaded and shot a third time and hit the coyote who was momentarily lifted upwards this time, but it recovered and disappeared over the hill's crest.

Jake just stood there looking at the shotgun like it had let him down, then he turned and started coming down. John and Jay got up off the ground and began walking up to Jake who said, "That's it! I'm getting a 12-gauge!"

Jay said, "Follow me."

They all three hiked up the hill. Lying there just over its crest was one dead coyote. How Jake had reloaded and shot twice after his first shot hitting the coyote all three times in such a short time was an amazing feat, but it had been so much fun to watch that it made Jay and John laugh.

They left for the ranch, dragging the coyote. Every time Jay or John looked back toward the hill. They said, "12-gauge! Ha!" and then they laughed some more.

John continued hiking. When he came to a butte overlooking Lucky Island, he sat down, taking in the view. He recalled the year all three of them had taken whitetail bucks from the island that had been created when the river had changed course due to erosion from spring flooding and left a dry riverbed surrounding a three-acre loop. The three acres were almost impenetrable with chokecherry bushes and plumb thickets plus snowberry shrubs covering every square inch. There were numerous cottonwood and ash trees towering above everything. It was a buck paradise!

The brothers could count on a whitetail buck or two being present every time they visited the island, but there were just too many escape routes. The only shots they were offered were deer running at full speed. They had become adept at running shots but always preferred stationary or walking shots to avoid wounding an animal.

One day, after another unsuccessful foray into the island with no one getting a clean shot, they sat down below the crest of a butte overlooking the island eating cold sandwiches, and they began brainstorming a better way to hunt the island. Suddenly, Jake blurted out "Sparrows!"

John and Jay looked at him and said, "What are you talking about?"

Jake answered, "We have got to hunt them like we used to hunt sparrows."

John and Jay looked at each other and realized Jake was right. Without any more discussion, they finished eating, went home, gathered some tools, and headed back to the island. Once they got there, they immediately began building a sniper's blind considering the prevalent wind direction and a minimal route into the blind with the least disturbance. They also built shooting lanes by chopping down numerous small trees and shrubs.

They stayed away for a week, then snuck in and shot three whitetail bucks in two days. They named the three-acre loop Lucky Island, and the brothers kept it a secret between them.

When John arrived at the cemetery, he was mentally exhausted. All he could think of as he sat on the ground in front of his brothers' graves was, "What have I done?" He sat in silence, his mind racing, searching for an answer.

After some time, he began to feel his brothers' presence and a calm feeling engulfed him. His mind cleared, and he knew that they had all tried to do the right thing by serving their country, even if it was for a lost cause. He felt extremely proud of his brothers and knew they wanted his new path to be with their parents. He could feel it coming from them.

John stood up, came to attention, and saluted his brothers. Then he said out loud, "Thank you for your service."

On the walk home, John hardly noticed Jay's draw, Jake's Hill, or Lucky Island. He was only focused on getting home to his parents.

Shirley called John the next day and apologized profusely. John told her that he was okay, and then he said, "We would never have been complete if we had tucked in our tails and ran like so many have done."

Shirley said. "I know. I spoke to Sally last night, and she said the same thing. It's something that we have admired about you and your brothers without realizing it. I now know what true sacrifice is, and I will always remember and honor veterans, especially you and your brothers."

John thanked Shirley for the apology and reminded her that he was available anytime she wanted to talk. After the conversation, John couldn't stop thinking about how perfect Shirley and Jake were for each other and what a wonderful life they would have had together. He hoped the best for her. He knew that now was the time for him to be what his brothers would have been.

BROTHERS NO MORE

THEY WENT TO WAR BECAUSE THEIR COUNTRY CALLED

ONE CAME HOME WHOLE

TWO CAME HOME IN BOXES

THEN THEY BECAME BROTHERS NO MORE

CHAPTER 16
Joan

After completing his two-year tour in the Army, John arrived back at the ranch with his whole life ahead of him. It seemed like he had been gone from home for half of his young life. All the memories of growing up on the ranch were there, but they just seemed so far into the past. Everything just seemed slightly different.

After Jake left, their bedroom in the basement seemed so empty that John could only spend time sleeping there. He just couldn't stop looking at Jay's bed and dresser along with all his personal belongings that Helen had kept in place. Then there was Jay's uniform with all his ribbons and other military trappings hanging in their closet. Even though John would have preferred to put Jay's things out of sight, he knew keeping them out in the open helped his mother.

John felt much older than his age and couldn't

yet imagine what life was going to be like going forward without Jay in it. If it hadn't been for his parents, John may have hit the road and not looked back, because everywhere he looked reminded him so much of Jay. His parents were supportive, and they faithfully kept Jay and Jake in their lives, and slowly brought them back into John's life.

Shortly after Jake died, Helen cleaned Jay and Jake's belongings out of the basement bedroom and removed their dad's uniform which had hung over the stairway to the basement for a long time. Where she put Jay and Jake's personal belongings and his dad's uniform was personal, but John knew they were treasured and in good hands. John could see that the past two years had taken a toll on his parents. They could use help running the ranch, and after Jake died, he had decided during his visit to the cemetery that he and the world owed them greatly for their sacrifices.

John decided to stay on the ranch. When he approached his parents, he knew that it was the right decision for them. Helen cried tears of joy as she grabbed John and said, "Thank you! We were worried that we might lose you."

Joe gave John a hug as he said, "It's good to have you safe and at home."

Slowly, the ranch began to ease John back into stability. The flow of life generated by livestock and the land renewed John, and he began to realize that the right decision for his parents had also become the right decision for him.

John still had a slight inkling for a college education and decided to take a few college classes in a local college located about 40 miles from the ranch. He would schedule three classes in the afternoon that wouldn't interfere too much with his ranch duties, and he'd drive back and forth every day.

John had decided to take a few accounting and business classes to help with the management and financial aspects of ranching. John's dad would have to do double duty during the afternoons, but Joe assured John that he was up to the task.

College is where John met Joan by accident, bumping into her while rushing between classes. He apologized profusely, introduced himself, and asked if he could take her to lunch for being such a klutz. To John's surprise, she accepted, and they met in the cafeteria the next day.

Joan was the oldest of five siblings and had grown up on a farm about 10 miles from the ranch where John had grown up. She had attended a different high school in another town because of school district boundaries.

John could remember seeing her in the past while attending dances at the local community hall. She had mesmerized him immediately with her haunting blue eyes, long curly auburn-tinged hair, and a distinct country complexion. She was dating someone else at the time, and John had thought how lucky that guy was. He even had a brief conversation with her one night and remembered her friendly, outgoing personality.

Joan was attending college with the intention of attaining a degree in elementary education. She was a very attentive, caring person, and John could see that she would become an outstanding teacher. He knew almost immediately that she was the person that he wanted to spend the rest of his life with, but he was terrified that she wouldn't feel the same.

After a short time, the apprehension disappeared, and he could feel them becoming closer than just friends. It was one of the greatest feelings that John had ever felt, and he just couldn't get enough of her company.

John came in early every day that he could, and they had lunch together. They began dating which eventually turned into much more. John asked Joan to marry him almost a year after bumping into her, and she accepted, but she wanted to first finish college and get her degree in teaching. They agreed to a long engagement, and they would see as much of each other as possible.

John could see that operating the ranch alone was taking too great of a toll on his dad, and eventually he stopped his college classes to devote time to the ranch and his future with Joan. They were married almost immediately after Joan graduated. John purchased a used trailer house which was moved to the ranch, and it became their home until both of his parents passed, and they moved into the ranch house.

The ranch house had been built by John's grandfather. John's mom and dad had built an addition onto the backside which more than doubled the original size of the home. The house needed new windows and siding. The plumbing and electrical systems were also in need of replacement. John and Joan had also decided to do some interior remodeling that included a new kitchen, additional bathrooms, and tearing down interior walls to open up the living area.

The couple hired contractors and stayed in the trailer until the remodeling was complete. John rebuilt the porch himself, and the place turned out looking pretty good, especially with Joan in it.

John also invested in newer equipment as they could afford it. Number one on the list was a tractor with a cab that featured air conditioning for Joan who helped with haying during the summers when she wasn't teaching. John also got rid of the square baler and purchased a large round baler that produced half-ton, round bales requiring considerably less time in the field to complete the baling process. He also sold the rakes and a pull-type mower and purchased a self-propelled hay swather that could mow and rake the hay in one pass.

When it was all finally acquired, the equipment enabled John, with the occasional assistance from Joan, to cut, bale, and haul the entire hay crop without having to hire help every summer to assist with the haying. John also used a loader tractor with a heated cab to feed livestock in the winter.

When it was possible, John and Joan attended every informational meeting presented in the area that pertained to ranching. Livestock health, nutrition, animal husbandry, and genetics plus range management, plant identification, and growing cycles of various prairie grasses were topics they sought out. Weed identification and control also became a priority. Local, state, and federal agricultural specialists were consulted, and any books pertaining to livestock and range management were purchased and judiciously studied. Magazines linked to the livestock industry were continually coming in the mail.

Management decisions were based on what they learned through research and trial and error. John and Joan were amazed at the positive results on the land and livestock plus the financial benefits that followed. John reminisced one day about some advice his dad had given him, "Take care of the land, and it will take of your cows, who will take care of you."

John and Joan became walking encyclopedias when it came to livestock care and land management, and they were occasionally requested to give presentations at conferences for land management and livestock production. They especially enjoyed sharing knowledge with youth, so much that they would often turn down a major speaking engagement to do a presentation for a local youth group.

ALIVE AGAIN

HAD TO ALMOST DIE

TO FEEL ALIVE AGAIN

CHAPTER 17
The Right Stuff

It was 9:00 a.m. when John stepped out on the front porch with a steaming cup of coffee to soak up some morning sun and enjoy the panoramic view that had been enjoyed by three generations of his family. The ranch house was located on a bluff overlooking the river bottoms, the lifeblood of the ranch. Everything revolved around the river bottoms. They produced the forage necessary to sustain the numerous ranch livestock through long grueling winters. The river bottoms also provided habitat for numerous species of wildlife. For three generations the family had used the bottoms to provide forage for the ranch's livestock and the wildlife that made their home within the ranch's boundaries.

The river bottoms were an alive, vibrant part of the ranch, and it always felt good to sit back occasionally to enjoy the view and reminisce about past times spent on the bottoms with his brothers and friends. John saw a vehicle crest the hill two miles to the southwest. Hunters, he assumed, for it was that time of the year, and it was a perfect day for a fall hunt.

There were already hunters who had prearranged permission to hunt for the day, but John didn't want to turn down anyone if possible. It was such a perfect day for hunting, and he had just been reminiscing about his brothers and the times that they had spent hunting the bottoms on days such as this. He really missed them and the times that they had spent together.

Well, John thought, *there's plenty of game and there's plenty of bottoms. If I send them over east, they won't interfere with the scheduled party due to arrive in a couple of hours.*

John was not pleased with the speed of the vehicle as it pulled into the yard. He was even less pleased when instead of asking permission to hunt, the hunters asked how much he charged to hunt on his land. John looked long and hard at the group and answered, "Well, boys, this ranch isn't for sale, never has been and it never will be. It's always been considered a treasure to be shared but only with people who appreciate and respect what they've been given access to. I suggest that you boys head down the road because we don't have much use for draft dodgers on this place."

When one of them asked why they were considered draft dodgers, John answered, "Isn't that a Jap vehicle you're driving? Well, I guess you'll just have to go to Japan and hunt there if they are who you're going to support. This is an American ranch. We buy American products and support American workers. My dad and uncles fought the Japs in the Philippines, and my brothers and I fought their cousins in Vietnam, and we'll be fighting another Asian country one of these days, so I suggest you all get your acts together before it's too late."

They left in more of a hurry than they had arrived, and John thought, *Boy, they must think I'm a real prejudiced jerk. Well, who cares? I lost two uncles in one war and two brothers in another, so maybe I have the right to be a little prejudiced about certain things.*

It was on days like this that he missed his brothers the most, for they had been inseparable as youths. *Maybe even a little too close*, he thought, and then he became overjoyed that they had been so close and enjoyed their lives together while they had lasted.

Their dad once said, "Live life to its fullest every day because you never know about tomorrow. If tomorrow comes, that's great, but if it doesn't, you'll know you did your best today."

Well, we sure did, John thought.

"Were those the hunters that were scheduled to hunt today?" Joan asked as she came out onto the porch to join John for a moment together.

"No," answered John. "Just some doorknobs

driving around wasting time. I'm going to ride out and check the north herd and maybe move them if the pasture tells me to."

John and Joan had implemented a rotational grazing program many years ago against the wishes of John's dad who deemed it just a lot of extra expense and work for nothing until he saw how the pastures improved and the extra weight gain on the cows and their calves in the fall. Then it became his idea, which he touted to anyone who would listen. John didn't mind. Even though his dad had doubts, he had allowed John and Joan to spend a fair amount of money putting in fences, running underground water lines, and purchasing water tanks. So, since his dad paid for it, maybe it should be his idea.

John asked Joan if she would check in the hunting party from town when they arrived and send them over west onto the old Tucker place. He added, "I've prepared a map to help them get there. It will be a Boy Scout troop led by a Mr. Johnson. I'm sorry, but I forgot his first name. They will be here in a couple of hours. I should be home about dark."

"Sure, no problem," Joan answered, "I'm going to be around the house today. Isn't it just beautiful out today? I always enjoy this view, especially on days like this."

"Yes," answered John as he left for the barn, "it's beautiful and so are you. See ya later."

Joan could tell that John wasn't having a very

good day. He loved kids and normally would have stayed and helped guide the party of youngsters, but she sensed they sometimes reminded him of himself and his brothers when they were growing up. The pain of never being able to ever see them again was just too much for him to bear.

Damn wars! Joan thought. *Why do people have to constantly fight one another?*

Then she remembered what John had once said. "It's not the people who go to war, it's the leaders. People just follow them."

She just couldn't understand. Why would people follow a leader into something as terrible as war? But John and his brothers had, and his dad and uncles had done the same thing. Doesn't one generation learn anything from the next? *Oh well*, Joan thought, *that's a legacy that won't be passed on, at least in this family.*

She often wondered how much being child-less really bothered John. Children were always something she had planned on in her life, but a greater power had decided otherwise. It had taken them a while to accept the fact that they would never be able to have children, and they had con-templated options available to them from adop-tion to foster care for a long time. They eventually decided to make as many children as possible a part of their lives—Joan, by becoming a teacher, and John, by opening the ranch to children and volunteering for every local youth program in their community.

Joan had two sisters and two brothers who all lived within reasonable distances of the ranch, and whenever they needed a break from their kids or a private vacation, they would bring their children over to stay with Joan and John. Joan's nieces and nephews were always welcome, and at times kept Joan and John extremely busy, but the visits were always worth the time and effort. John thoroughly enjoyed the visits, and he became impressed with one nephew who, despite growing up in town, became interested in every aspect of ranching and expressed a desire to make agriculture his future. It made John feel good to know that maybe the ranch could someday be passed on to one of Joan's nieces or nephews.

Interacting with other people's children was rewarding, and it sometimes made them feel a little empty at the same time. They had both adjusted, and just like living off the land, they took what they could get when they could get it and had an impact on as many children as possible.

John saddled his favorite horse, T-2, who was named after his dad's legendary horse Traveler. Traveler was a beautiful dapple gray who lived into his twenties despite the rigors of ranch work placed upon him. He had been a legend within the local community because of his athletic abilities and intelligence that enabled him to perform multiple tasks with great skill. His speed and endurance were also legendary. He was never beaten in a race until his later years, and whenever there was hard riding that needed to be done, Dad and Traveler's help was always requested.

Traveler's most legendary trait was that he would allow only his owner and children to ride him. Many neighbors had tried, but Traveler could also have been a legendary bucking horse. Why he would let their dad put young children on him and give them leisurely rides was a mystery that no one could ever figure out.

Traveler became a big babysitter for their dad that he used for all three of the brothers. John could still remember his early rides on Traveler. It didn't matter how hard he tried to make him run or direct him out of the yard. Traveler would just keep plodding around the ranch buildings at a leisurely gait, putting up with John's antics until his dad would come to his rescue.

He could also remember the day that his mom caught him riding Traveler around the yard. She had seen Traveler in action with strange riders trying to ride him. Dad took the brunt of her outrage, but he finally calmed her down and had her watch John riding Traveler, trying to make him run or change his route around the ranch buildings. She left, still upset, with a very stern warning to Joe about his legendary horse. T-2 wasn't even close to being as great as Traveler, but he was a good horse, and he had a few traits which reminded John of his dad's horse.

As John left the yard, he felt guilty for not staying and helping Mr. Johnson with his Boy

Scout troop, but he knew he would not be a positive influence today because of his state of mind. Look at how he had handled those hunters. Not that they didn't have it coming, but that was no excuse for being rude. He knew that his dad would have been disappointed.

"Don't become like them," he would say. "It's their problem if they want to live their lives like that. Don't let them bring you down to their level."

John thought he'd failed that day, or was his dad trying to make him perfect because he was the only one left? *No*, he thought, *Dad tried to raise all three of us the same way, the right way.*

It must have been extremely hard on both his mother and father to have sent three sons to war and only have one come back, but they rarely showed it. They only showed pride that their sons had answered their country's call to serve. Even though they didn't fully understand the conflict in Vietnam, they believed in their country's involvement and would become very upset with anyone who didn't show support for our country's fighting men.

John's parents began doing one thing every Veterans Day after Jay and Jake had died that was both a mystery and intriguing. They would disappear for the entire day. No one ever knew where they went or what they did for the day. The day before Veterans Day, Mom would pack food and Dad would gas up the car. They would get up early and leave before the sun was up and not come home until after dark.

They never spoke about what they did or where they went. It was a total mystery. John and Joan talked about it and were always dying to ask his parents what they were doing for the day but knew better. They always came back renewed and in great spirits.

After John's dad passed, his mom would disappear by herself until she became unable to drive. John would offer to take her, but she would refuse, and he didn't push the issue. Wherever she and his dad had gone and done was private, and it would remain a mystery. John honored his mom's wishes and never pushed the issue, but Joan and he always wondered.

When John's mom passed, he had to go in to see their attorney for an official reading of the will and other associated legal estate matters. When the lists of assets and property were reviewed, John discovered his parents owned a section of land in Montana along the Yellowstone River about 140 miles from the ranch.

Among the title documents for the Montana property was a handwritten note from his dad with a name, address, and phone number of a Mr. Bob Hannsen. John was supposed to contact him in Montana concerning the property. John was mystified. What other surprises did his parents have in store?

John contacted Mr. Hannsen that evening, and he seemed to be a very nice fellow. He knew

John's parents very well and lived close to the property. He also knew all about John and his wife, Joan. He advised John to make a trip out to Montana to view the property immediately and told John, "Once you see and experience it, you'll have the answers to a lot of questions about your parents."

John told Mr. Hannsen he would need a few days to get things on the ranch in order, but Joan and he could be there in three days. Mr. Hannsen said, "That's exactly what your dad told me you would say. I'm looking forward to meeting you both. Call me when you get to Montana, and I'll give you directions and meet you at the property."

When John and Joan arrived at the entrance to the mystery property, they were met by Bob Hannsen. He was a young, polite, western rancher, and they immediately felt like they were in the company of an old friend.

He opened a gate and said, "Follow me." They drove in on a well-built graveled road and followed it through the property. Bob stopped occasionally to point out a cross fence, stock tank, and other improvements that John's dad and he had made to the property since his dad had acquired it. The road led to a small, one-room, log cabin that featured a huge deck placed on a bluff overlooking the Yellowstone River. The view was breathtaking.

Mr. Hannsen pulled out a key and said, "Here's the key. Go on in. There are a lot of answers in that cabin you need to see. I'll be back in a while to answer any other questions you have."

When John and Joan entered, they were overwhelmed by what they saw. To their left were four beautifully built display cases enclosed in glass that went from the floor to the ceiling side by side on one end wall of the cabin. Three of the cases contained military uniforms hung up in front of a red, white, and blue background. There was a name plate with dates of service and various medals and accommodations displayed. One contained Jay's uniform and medals, one was Jake's, and one was their dad's, all of them done up the same. The fourth display case was empty. It would be for John someday.

The displays were awesome! John was completely taken over by emotion. To their right a rock fireplace encompassed the other end wall. The front of the cabin featured two huge windows which displayed the breathtaking view of the Yellowstone River. In the center of the room were two large leather chairs with a log end table in between them set at an angle to allow viewing the display cases and the view through the front windows in unison.

The back wall featured a three-foot glass display case that ran the entire length of the room. It was filled with various items accumulated by the brothers while growing up. Their first gun was even there on display. Each item invoked a memory from the brothers' lives. Above the display case were pictures that chronicled the three brothers' lives from birth.

There was a small, stoutly-built log table with two log chairs near the fireplace and two log deck chairs outside on the deck. An outhouse had also been constructed out back with a paved trail leading to it.

John could imagine his parents sitting in the leather chairs or out on the front deck. Now, he understood. This was where they brought their pain and left it every Veterans Day. The place was special, and John and Joan sat as his parents had and discussed what to do with it.

They had it all planned out by the time Bob returned with his wife, Carol, and a lunch basket which she'd prepared. They brought in the two deck chairs and arranged them around the table as they had done many times with John's parents.

When Bob asked for questions, John leaned forward and said, "Please tell me the story."

Bob began with the beginning of Carol and his ranching venture. They were young and in debt up to their ears when this adjoining land came up for sale. Bob and Carol desperately tried to secure funds to purchase the property, but they were turned down by every bank in the area. They were told they had too much debt and not enough collateral. Disappointed, they found out that the property had been purchased by an out-of-state party, but they vowed to be good neighbors to whomever had purchased the property.

Then one day John's parents showed up with

an offer too good to be true. For the right to use the section of land for grazing and haying, Bob and Carol were to pay the annual property taxes, supply labor for improvements, and clean and maintain a cabin which was going to be built. Bob said the deal was sealed with a handshake, and if it hadn't been for John's parents, they probably wouldn't have been able to succeed and stay on their ranch. Bob added that they were very grateful for what John's dad had done for them over the years. If John and Joan were going to sell the property, Carol and he would be very interested in purchasing it but could not pay what it would bring through a realtor or auction.

Bob said, "This section would bring top dollar as a hunting and recreational property, and the people who would be purchasing it have got a lot more money than we have."

John answered, "This is what Joan and I have decided to do with the place. Would you and Carol like to continue the previous arrangement that you had with my parents, only it would be with Joan and me? When both of us have passed, the property will be willed to your family. You'll have to have it appraised and pay some taxes plus attorney fees created by the transfer, but it will be yours."

Bob and Carol both began protesting and were adamant about paying for the land at a fair price that John and Joan would be comfortable with. "Your parents have given us so much already, and this wouldn't be fair to both of you," Bob blurted out.

John replied, "I'm all that's left. We have no heirs. My parents have left us so much, and Joan and I know in our hearts that this is what my parents would have wanted. Whether or not you realize it, you two and your family were adopted by my parents. You two were a godsend for my parents. You gave them strength and inspiration. My parents didn't travel much, only to visit relatives. During their later years, we noticed they were visiting relatives and friends in Montana a lot, and upon returning, they were so exuberant and at ease with life. We always felt good when they would announce a trip to Montana because it seemed to help them so much." John stood up and extended his hand, "Now, do we have a deal?"

Bob and Carol went outside to discuss the arrangement. When they returned, they reluctantly agreed but only under certain terms. They would pay an annual rent plus the annual taxes plus they'd pay all repair costs and maintain the cabin exactly as they had been doing for John's parents. John and Joan agreed, and the deal was sealed with a handshake.

From that day forward, John and Joan continued his parents' tradition, and every Veterans Day they would get up early and make the trip to Montana. Joan could tell that the visits to his parents' memorial were healing for John, and the money they had lost on the property was immaterial. John's healing was priceless just as it had been for his parents. Joan also knew the Montana property had been handled just as John's parents had hoped it would be. What wise people they had been! After that, the first thing Joan would do upon entering the property was say a silent thank-you to John's parents.

THE NAM

RAN FROM THE WAR FOR A LONG TIME

NEVER ANNOUNCING ANY PARTICIPATION

NOBODY EVER PROBED VERY DEEP

I MIGHT HAVE ESCAPED

IF IT HADN'T COME BACK IN BITS AND PIECES

CHAPTER 18
Christmas Party

Joan talked John into attending a Christmas party they were both invited to by the college they had both attended. The college had started a farm and ranch management academic program for students wanting to pursue a career within agriculture.

John allowed the department to bring students out to the ranch to perform research projects varying from pasture management and forage production to livestock husbandry. The students occasionally got in the way of ranch functions and required physical and sometimes minimal financial assistance from John and Joan for various projects at times, but the students were inspiring and well worth the effort. They were the future of agriculture, and it was always interesting to gain their perspectives. At times John thought that he was learning more than the stu-

237

dents were.

The main entertainment at the Christmas party was a fashion show presented by the college drama department depicting United States military conflicts of the twentieth century. A male model dressed in a correct military period uniform and a female model dressed appropriately for the time period entered the stage and presented themselves while a monologue describing the conflict was presented. It was very well done and had apparently taken time and effort to produce.

It was very patriotic and entertaining, and the show received positive comments from everyone present. The show began with the Spanish-American War of 1898 and continued through the Desert Storm conflict, but Vietnam hadn't been included. Looking over at John's reaction, Joan knew immediately what she had to do.

She suddenly began feigning stomach pains and asked John if they could leave the party because of the discomfort. They politely apologized and exited the party.

John was quiet on the drive back to the ranch, and Joan could only guess his thoughts. She told him she was sorry for the lack of respect shown to Vietnam veterans, and she said that was going to have a talk with the college about it. Joan knew that the damage had been done and nothing could change it. She knew that most people didn't realize what John, many other veterans, and their families experienced daily.

Joan had been scared at first when she saw a pistol on John's nightstand, but eventually she became used to it being there. She was grateful when he purchased a small tabletop safe that was only large enough for one handgun to be stored in. John had also insisted that Joan know the code to open the safe and how to load and shoot the handgun stored in it.

She never did understand how John could be dead asleep after a long day working outside on the ranch and instantly awaken from any small noise, grab the pistol, and stealthily leave the bedroom to investigate the source of the disturbance. At first she would lie in bed nervously waiting for him to return and explain what had caused the event. After a while she became accustomed to his night ventures, but they usually interrupted her sleep.

One year after selling the annual calf crop, they bought a huge refrigerator-freezer unit. Joan had insisted on an ice maker. After it had woke John up multiple times during the first week, she had to begin turning the ice maker off every night before going to bed after John had threatened to tear it out of the refrigerator.

He would also get up during the night when he couldn't fall back asleep after waking up from a war dream. He would take the pistol from the safe and end up in one of the two huge leather recliners they had purchased for one of their wedding anniversaries and begin reading one of the many books they had accumulated. He would either read until the sun came up or fall asleep in the recliner.

Joan was glad John never spoke about his war dreams, but she worried when he would wind up spending multiple nights out in the recliner. She would offer her attention if he wanted someone to speak to about his dreams. All he would do is give her a big hug and thank her for the offer, then tell her that he was okay, especially with her in his life. Joan could only imagine the part of his life he never shared, but he seemed to handle it with a sense of awareness and stability that always amazed her.

While driving home, John began remembering encounters he and fellow soldiers had endured while traveling to deployments. Some airports kept military personal separated from the public with chain link fences. If there were anti-war protesters present inside of an airport terminal protesting, MPs would be posted at the airport's entrance points, and all military personnel were directed to an airport bar.

MPs would be stationed at the bar entrance. You were not allowed to leave or consume alcohol until your flight was announced. Sometimes you were escorted by MPs to your flight. The bar areas could become contemptuous places where the troops felt despised and dishonored while being forcefully separated from the public. Talk of taking care of the demonstrators would begin casually and sometimes escalate, creating an uncontrollable mob atmosphere.

That is exactly what happened when John was flying home in uniform for the last time. The primary instigator was a PFC (private first class), a former college student. He had turned his college education, funded by his parents, into one big party, and he ended up being drafted. He claimed his dad was pulling strings to get him either released or assigned to a stateside assignment.

Listening to him was taxing, and as people started to distance themselves from him, he directed the tirade toward the hippie protesters. It was hard to fathom why the group of soldiers who couldn't stand the guy just minutes earlier were now preparing to follow him through the MPs stationed at the door into the lobby area to physically confront the protesters.

As John was standing in the middle of the room trying to figure out how to diffuse the situation, an E-6 sergeant grabbed him and said, "I'm placing myself between the MPs and this mob. You take care of him." He pointed to the PFC college boy.

John waited for the sergeant to get in position, then he motioned for the PFC to come over to him. The PFC approached John, chanting with one fist raised above his head. When he got close enough, John punched the PFC with two swift punches, one in the midsection and one between the eyes. This caused the PFC to collapse onto the floor unable to get up.

The mood instantly changed in the room as troops looked over at their fallen leader. They became quiet and submissive, instantly following every order the E-6 sergeant gave them while maintaining a safe distance from John.

Oh, damn! John thought, *The MPs! I'm going to get arrested over this piece of shit!*

When he looked over at the senior MP, all the MP did was give John a thumbs-up sign. The MP then commanded some of the nearby troops to help him get the busted-up PFC to a medical aid station located in the airport.

"Well, he ain't too smart for a college boy," the E-6 sergeant said to John. "I'd buy you a drink, but the bar is closed. Will you take an IOU?"

When John explained how the incident could have extended his two-year tour with a stint in the brig, the sergeant shook his head and said, "Now *that* would not have made me feel good. Seeing the college boy sprawled out on the floor, *that* made me feel good. Thank you for sticking your neck out. Are you sure you don't want to re-enlist? The Army needs more men like you."

"No thanks," John said.

The sergeant shook John's hand and said, "I'm glad I met you." Then they parted ways, one headed overseas for his second tour in Vietnam, and one headed home to life as a civilian.

John remembered the exhilaration and relief he had felt upon boarding the freedom bird loaded with fellow soldiers that would take them home from Vietnam. Even though they were complete strangers, there was a common bond and respect conveyed.

Once he was processed and sent home, it became a whole new experience. The first thing he noticed was the avoidance exhibited by other travelers and the indifference directed toward him. A young woman angrily asked him not to sit near her in the lobby waiting area to which John politely replied, "Sorry, ma'am!" as he respectfully moved away which seemed to surprise her.

John thought about how odd and ironic it was that if there were other soldiers in the airline waiting area or on a civilian flight, they were immediately drawn together like magnets. Sharing as soldiers one last emotion from their military service together before taking the uniforms off—rejection.

John felt good about how soldiers were currently being welcomed home and honored for their service. Then he thought about how people from his generation always expressed concerns about the next generation, and he caught himself shaking his head just like his dad used to do.

When they got home, John told Joan that he had become so upset that he had contemplated canceling the student research project agreement they had with the college, but he finally realized that canceling the agreement would harm the students more than the college.

"But the college for sure isn't going to be included in our wills," he said.

Joan agreed, and she guaranteed that when she got done dealing with the college, they would never forget Vietnam veterans again. "They may even have a statue built," she proudly stated.

John shook his head, laughing, and said, "You and your statues. It seems like you think everyone should have one."

Then he fixed himself a rum and Coke with ice, grabbed a book, and headed for one of the leather recliners. Before Joan left for the bedroom, she gave John a kiss with a plea, "Now, don't stay up all night, promise?"

John lifted his drink and said, "Don't worry, I won't. I'm just going to sit here for a while, read a bit, and celebrate the fact that I'm not one of those college guys."

NEW GUY

LAID YOU INTO A BODY BAG AT DUSK

YOU WERE ONE OF US AT DAWN

NOW YOU'RE SOMEWHERE BACK IN THE WORLD

JUST CAN'T REMEMBER YOUR NAME

CHAPTER 19
Draft Dodger

It was a crisp, late fall morning and John had decided to go into town for morning coffee. He went in about once a month.

The same morning crowd was congregated in a back corner of Bob's Mini Mart and Gas Station complex. It was the only business besides a bar down the street left in what used to be a vibrant small town. Most of the morning crowd consisted of local farmers, and the rest were retired residents from the area. The major daily topics discussed were the weather, crops, local gossip, and reminiscing about the past.

John would notice that his brothers were never mentioned in any conversations about the past. It was like they had never existed. If he tried to inject them into a conversation, the others would become extremely uncomfortable.

It saddened and frustrated John that his

brothers were never mentioned. John would sometimes find himself judging the other coffee drinkers by their military service or lack of service. This led to him feeling guilty, and he'd have to remind himself of one of his dad's proverbs, "You can judge a man by what he has or hasn't done, but don't forget to also judge him by who he has become."

John tried to turn the conversations in a positive direction as much as possible. One morning, a younger neighbor was complaining about a veterinarian bill that his wife had brought home after trying to save their family dog who had been run over accidentally. "And then on top of that," he said, "I had to pay for the vet to put the dog to sleep."

John leaned back and said, "I guess I'm so old that I can remember when the cost of a vet bill was the price of a 22 shell."

"Well," the younger neighbor said shaking his head, "that's one I'll never tell my wife." Then he stopped, sat there contemplating, and said, "Maybe I will. I just won't give her any names." Then he paused again in thought and said, "She'll keep pestering me for a name, but I promise you, John. I'll give her the name of someone she doesn't like."

They all had a good laugh that morning, but coffee in town was usually a tiring and frustrating event for John. He was always the first one to head home.

John had tried to connect with other vets

when he first returned, and he even joined the local Legion Club. He soon grew tired of constantly listening to their stories and viewpoints. No one ever probed very deep into John's military odyssey, and he assumed it was because of his two brothers.

One evening at the Legion bar after a monthly meeting, another vet who'd rubbed John the wrong way one too many times and was very intoxicated walked up to John and asked sarcastically, "Have you ever killed anyone?"

Without thinking, John jumped up and got into his face screaming, "Killing has always been easy for me! It's living with it that isn't easy." The intoxicated vet backed away and left the bar immediately.

Word spread fast, especially in a small community, and things were never the same after that. John quit the Legion a short while later. No one ever bothered to ask him why or to reconsider. John became disillusioned with veteran clubs and vowed to avoid them in the future.

About a year after John had quit the Legion Club, a local legionnaire called to inform John that they were erecting a memorial wall for all the veterans from the county. The legionnaire asked John if he would like his and his brothers' names inscribed on the memorial wall. He also informed John that it would cost him $100 per name.

John lost his composure when he heard that last part. He curtly answered, "Yes, I would greatly appreciate and be honored to have my brothers and my name inscribed on the memorial, but I'm not going to pay for it. My brothers and I have already paid our dues! There's plenty of draft dodgers around, and you know who they are. They should step up and be responsible for all the costs associated with the memorial. It's the least they can do."

John was distraught after the call. His brothers deserved to have their names placed on the memorial wall. He contemplated paying for them and not himself but just couldn't bring himself to do it. They were brothers and brothers belonged together.

John contacted the Legion and offered to pay for his dad's and uncle's names, but he was told that there was going to be no charge for his dad because of everything he had done for the Legion Club over the years, and they were including his uncle for free. Later that year, a neighbor stopped in one day and mentioned how good it felt to see John's and his brothers' names together on the new memorial wall along with his dad and uncle.

John had resolved to never visit the memorial but today he would. It was very meaningful to see all their names together on the memorial wall and he thought, *Well, there's at least one decent draft dodger out there. Thank you, whoever you are!*

One morning while Joan and he were sitting on the porch having coffee and enjoying the view, he asked her if she had any thoughts about why he felt shunned by some people in the community. She looked at him thoughtfully and said, "Because they know you and your brothers did the right thing, standing up and fighting for your country, which is what a lot of them didn't do."

THE COST OF FREEDOM

WE ALL CARRY IT

ON OUR BACKS

SOME CARRY IT

MORE THAN OTHERS

BUT CARRY IT

WE MUST

FINAL REFLECTION FROM LEE REBSOM

This story is fiction inspired by real events. I served two tours in Vietnam, not as an LRRP, but mostly in the bush on various military watercraft. One of my brothers followed me to Vietnam, but due to injuries, he was medevaced home and discharged from duty early. He died in a car crash a year and a half after being discharged.

Many Vietnam Veterans unknowingly suffered from moral injury that was imposed upon them when they returned from the war. Some were personally confronted, most were just pushed aside and ignored. For some, the moral injury became a confusing aspect of their post-traumatic stress disorders. My greatest hope is for a continuation of the respect and gratitude currently being displayed towards military personnel. They deserve and appreciate it more than you will ever realize.

ABOUT THE AUTHOR

Lee Rebsom grew up in rural southwestern North Dakota on a farm and ranch. When he retired, one of the first things he did was create a bucket list. Writing a book was on the list. Because writing was completely out of his realm, it created a whole new learning experience. With the help of great people teaching and supporting him, writing this book became a reality.

Lee still lives in southwestern North Dakota with Harriette, his wife of 49 years. They both worked full time while raising two daughters and have since added a son-in-law and one very special granddaughter. After Lee retired from a major agribusiness company and Harriette retired from her job as a geriatric nurse, they inherited her parents' ranch, which helps keep Lee busy.

Lee's education consists of a two-year degree in farm and ranch and agribusiness management. He has never stopped learning, and he's now focused on learning all he can to improve the soil health and plant life on their ranch.

Lee reads a lot and likes to hunt. Calling coyotes has become one of his main hobbies, maybe because it's a continual learning experience.

Next on Lee's bucket list is the Maah Daah Hey Trail, a 144-mile single track bike and hiking trail through the Badlands of North Dakota. He hopes his body will hold up for that one.

To contact author Lee Rebsom or order signed copies of his book, e-mail him at: LeeRebsom@gmail.com

Unsigned books are available on Amazon

Made in the USA
Las Vegas, NV
06 April 2023

70271000R00149